HOLD ON, BABY!

"*Hold On, Baby!* is a great read for anyone navigating infertility. It's full of truths, lessons, healing and hope. A must-read for anyone in need of emotional healing."

—**Cheryl Dowling,** Founder, The IVF Warrior

"Lisa White is the IVF friend and guide 'who gets it' that you are looking for! Hold on to your Kleenex as Lisa shares her heart through personal stories and the soul work that helped her successfully navigate her IVF journey."

—**Linda Crawford,** OTR/L, Founder, BraveTherapy.net

"Lisa White guides you step-by-step through a process that is sure to transform any fear you have around infertility or IVF. A warm and loving reminder that you can trust your body and your life. This book will change you in positive and surprising ways."

—**Aubry Hoffman,** Author of *Activate Your Light*

"A good beginning for those embarking upon the IVF process."

—**Pamela Cohen Hirsch,** Founder, Baby Quest Foundation, Inc.

"A soulful yet practical guide to the journey of infertility. Lisa White's experience will inspire you, while journaling prompts help the reader navigate and explore their personal experience more in depth. This is a useful, relatable, heartfelt guide for anyone embarking on a fertility journey."

—Jeffrey Faudem, L.Ac., FBORM, Dipl.,
Certified Acupuncturist and Herbalist, Denverfertility.com

"Lisa White is an infertility warrior reflecting on her own experience and offering a lifeline to others who are struggling with infertility. She explores the emotional rollercoaster, provides reassurance, and offers supportive tips for surviving and thriving through the family-building journey."

—Lora Shahine, M.D., R.E., Pacific Northwest Fertility, Author of *Not Broken: An Approachable Guide to Miscarriage and Recurrent Pregnancy Loss*

"*Hold On, Baby!* shouts from the rooftops important messages that our world needs to hear right now: Hope beckons. Be brave. Don't give up. Stay connected. Be patient. The words are suffuse with soul wisdom and will be a steady companion for your journey."

—Sarah Davison-Tracy, Author, Speaker, Founder, Seeds of Exchange

Hold On, Baby!

modern wisdom
P R E S S

Modern Wisdom Press
Boulder, Colorado, USA
www.modernwisdompress.com

Published 2020

Cover Design: Maryl Swick

Author's photo courtesy of Britt Nemeth of Britt Nemeth Studios

MEDICAL DISCLAIMER

The information in this book is a result of years of practical experience by the author. This information is not intended as a substitute for the advice provided by your physician or other healthcare professional. Do not use the information in this book for diagnosing or treating a health problem or disease, or prescribing medication or other treatment.

Hold On, Baby!

A soulful guide to Riding the Ups and Downs of Infertility and IVF

LISA WHITE

For Olivia.

You are the brightest light and a part of my soul forever.
Thank you for choosing me as your mama.

In memory of my mom.

Your love is with me always.

Contents

Foreword

MOST OF US TAKE FOR GRANTED OUR ABILITY TO START A family. As a result, we tend to delay our plans until we're absolutely sure that we're ready to alter our lifestyle enough to become parents. Then the reality sets in. It can take time. In fact, it can take a lot more time to initiate a pregnancy than most people imagine. Along the way, we often get diverted by unplanned obstacles—like the COVID19 challenge that caused major shifts in all aspects of our society—or by personal challenges like undiagnosed conditions. My guess is that you're reading this book because you've come up against some of these challenges.

As a fertility specialist, I have dedicated my professional career to helping people become parents. Yet my wife and I didn't originally plan to have children. It wasn't until she had turned 40 that we changed our minds. As a result, we only tried to conceive for a few months before we chose to use the science that we offered our patients to help us achieve our goal. We knew the chances of success would be modest without medical intervention. And yet, despite our knowledge and experience, going through fertility treatment was a humbling process.

I was more than 10 years into my career as a fertility specialist and was fully informed of our prognosis. Still, after several failed ovulation induction-insemination cycles, a failed IVF attempt and a biochemical pregnancy—it felt much more real and very personal. Experiencing the delays, the setbacks and the failed attempts made me more fully appreciate the emotional aspects of infertility that my patients endure. Although I don't believe that going through this challenge changed the way I approach fertility treatment with my patients, it did make me more fully aware of the need to help my patients feel empowered and emotionally supported on their journey. That's why when Lisa invited me to support her efforts to nurture women going through fertility treatment, I enthusiastically accepted.

Lisa White is a kind and optimistic woman who met and overcame many obstacles to become the mom that she is today. Instead of coming through the process feeling fatigued—she was emboldened. She learned, through her own experience, several important techniques and tips to carry her through her journey. Not long after the birth of her daughter, she reached out to me to express her desire to share her earned knowledge to help others on this path. Her resilience inspired me in a very personal way. I leapt at the opportunity to support her efforts to mentor others, like you, with her knowledge and experience.

I continue to pursue new techniques to further boost the success of modern fertility treatments. Yet I am still haunted by the loss of the opportunity to work with women/couples that drop out of treatment prematurely due to the emotional challenge. We don't all experience stress equally. That's why having more tools for stress management and emotional support can only improve your health/ wellness while you pursue your pregnancy. There is even evidence that it might improve your chance of achieving the goal of having a healthy baby. As you consider the tips offered on these pages, I hope that *Hold On, Baby!* becomes a useful tool on your successful journey towards parenthood.

With kindness and optimism,

Robert A. Greene, MD, FACOG
Board Certified Fertility Specialist
(and successful fertility patient)
Conceptions Reproductive Associates of Colorado

Introduction

"You are a child of the universe, no less than the trees and the stars; you have a right to be here. And whether or not it is clear to you, no doubt the universe is unfolding as it should."

—MAX EHRMANN

THE SEED TO WRITE THIS BOOK WAS PLANTED SHORTLY AFTER giving birth to my daughter. Five months after to be exact. Some people say a lot of creativity can flow out of you after giving birth, and that was true for me. I was flooded with inspiration and ideas to bring forth into the world. I knew I could turn my *"wounds into wisdom,"* as Oprah Winfrey has shared about her experiences.

My Why

I wrote this book to help women and couples struggling through the emotional rollercoaster of going through in vitro fertilization (IVF) to get pregnant. I want to help shift the perception that this process has to be hard and painful. It can be another way. I'm not saying it will be easy, but *it's worth it.* I remember the moment when I was struck with pursuing a new purpose while I was holding my five-month-old girl in my arms. It hit me. I heard the message loud and clear—help support other women going through IVF, share your story, and be a beacon of hope. Many downloads came to me. All of the out-of-the-box ways I went about this journey needed to be told.

1

I have an intention to write a book.

I wrote this in my journal in February of 2018. The idea was born. It has now morphed into the book you are reading.

I never anticipated having to walk the road of infertility. Although it's a part of my story, I didn't let it define me, and I certainly wasn't going to let it write its own ending. I'm sharing my experience as a fellow fertility sister and IVF warrior in the hopes that this book may bring some hope and comfort to you in times of struggle. You may feel as if you've hit rock bottom and are grasping for a lifeline. I was there too. You wonder how you're going to make it through all the tears, the shots, and the dreams you hold for your future. Know this: It's when we fall that we often discover our inherent power. These low points teach us more than any of the highs we get from standing on the mountaintops. It's my desire that you will gain new insights as you go through your fertility journey and that you'll be reminded of how strong you really are.

We all have to deal with adversity in life. It's one of the things that shapes us into who we are. I know you can think of a time you faced adversity and overcame it. Our ability to get up and move forward despite the obstacles and hardships we face is what strengthens us. We build courage. We build our resilience muscles. You might feel infertility has caused you to fall down and that it seems impossible to get back up. This road will test you. It will challenge you, but it will also transform you. It is possible to get back up. This book will show you the way.

When you first embark on the path of IVF you face a lot of un-knowns. It can often feel daunting. It takes bravery to step forward on this path. Begin to embrace the possibilities rather than succumb to your fears. When you embrace the possibilities, you feel more hopeful and you add more joy and fun to your life. It's a magical way of thinking. I invite you to try it out.

I remember journaling what **brave** meant to me on my journey:

> *Brave is going through IVF. It's the courage to do another cycle. It's taking all the hormones and shots. It's wanting a baby so badly that you will go through this process and have to let go of control. Everything is unknown. It's not knowing the outcome but doing it anyway.*

You, my friend, are brave. You are courageous, and you need to be reminded of your power.

Consider this fertility challenge a chapter of your life. You will have many more chapters in your life. I hope my book serves as a support for you on your path to motherhood.

The poem that follows was written for me by a woman I discovered on a sidewalk in downtown Denver. She had an old-fashioned typewriter in front of her with a sign saying, "Pick a subject. Get a poem." I was intrigued and knew I had to connect with her. This sweet poem is a gift that I treasure. May it warm your heart as it does mine. It hangs in our bedroom as a reminder of the magic and joy to be found in this journey of a lifetime.

Blessings to you on your mothering journey.

All my love,

Lisa

Getting Pregnant

We come closer
To the dream
Of our own
Kid crawling
Thru the mountains
Of our lives, continuing
The love we express
Day after day—
Imagination
Bursting
With first words—
We nurture ourselves
Thru the challenges—
Wisdom expanding,
Hope like a prayer
To the sky.

—Abigail Mott
Denver, Colorado
11/25/16

Chapter 1

Fasten Your Seatbelt

THIS MAY JUST BE THE RIDE OF YOUR LIFE. HOLD ON, BABY!

If you are reading this book, my fertility sister and fellow warrior, then I've already accomplished what I set out to do. This book was inspired by my own personal journey going through IVF. I'm writing to you, dear one. I want you to *hold on* to your dream, *hold on* to hope, and *hold on* for the day when you come through to the other side. The rollercoaster of emotions on the IVF journey may throw you around a bit, so buckle in. This ride will challenge you and transform you. Trust the guidance within these pages and use it to send the message out to your little one: *Hold on, baby. I'm coming for you.*

When I embarked on our fertility journey, there was no guide to support me. My husband and I were pretty naïve about the process of IVF and the road that lay ahead. I thought things would happen in the exact timeline I had envisioned. I dreamed of the option to choose the number of embryos to transfer. *Would we choose to transfer one? Would we try to go for twins? What if the embryo, or embryos, split?* I even wondered if we would choose the gender of our first baby. So many questions came to mind, and I thought things would go quickly with no real bumps along the way.

Girl, I was wrong.

You don't know what you don't know. My husband and I had not done a lot of prior research about IVF and all things related to infertility. Our clinic gave us a mini course on the process of IVF, on possible procedures, medications, and routine appointments. I was not prepared for one important thing: all of the waiting. *Lots of waiting.* I know you can relate to the emotional toll this brings. If you think IVF is an express ticket to motherhood, it certainly is not. The information often comes at you pretty fast, and when that first big box of medication arrives, you start to feel the anxiety creep up inside. At least it did for me.

Facing the Fears

There are so many fears that arise when you begin the process of IVF. During the initial testing period, you face many unknowns, but it's a crucial place to start. It is essential to get medical advice on your unique situation as you move forward in the decision-making process.

You may go to a class to learn about the steps in an IVF cycle, how an egg retrieval works, and what happens during an embryo transfer, but until you're really *in* it, you don't have any idea what's involved. You are bombarded with a new lingo of abbreviations and terms. It can often feel as if this process is taking over your entire life. Between the medications, the frequent appointments for monitoring, blood draws, and tracking your schedule, it can feel so overwhelming. I remember these feelings well.

One of the hardest parts is the waiting and wondering. *Is this all going to work out?* Reality sank in when I started to ask myself some pretty tough questions. Fears came up. *Would I become a mom? Would I be able to have biological children?* I had never imagined not being able to have children of my own, but the thought became very real.

You often feel like a failure when you are having difficulty conceiving and allowing your body to do what it was intended to do. You may blame yourself for the situation you are in, but I'm here to tell you this is *not* your fault. Feeling the shame of infertility is common, and sadly, it only contributes to the inner pain you experience. We often think, *"What is wrong with me?"* These words take hold, and unfortunately, you may start to adopt these beliefs. I'll say it again: There is nothing wrong with you. These are limiting beliefs. They are not serving you, and we're going to squash them right away. But before we do that, I want you to know that *I get it.*

The Pain is Real

I've walked this path, and I know how painful it can be when you want nothing more than to be a mother or grow your family. You may know the daunting statistic that one in eight individuals are going through infertility. You may have experienced heartbreak with negative pregnancy tests, failed Intrauterine Insemination (IUI) or IVF cycles, loss of embryos not making it to blastocysts, or no viable embryos at all. Maybe you've made the decision to move to donor eggs, donor sperm, or donor embryos, or you've chosen a surrogate to carry your child. Maybe you've experienced the heartbreak of a miscarriage or multiple miscarriages. The sad statistic is that one in four women have experienced this devastating loss. Although I have never experienced a miscarriage, I do know what real loss feels like. In this book, you'll learn about one of the biggest losses I was going through outside of infertility. I was confronted with losing my mom to a long-standing illness. It truly was the hardest time in my life.

I understand the feeling of just trying to breathe and keep your head above water. Each day can feel like you're drowning when you're in the midst of fertility challenges. You often lose sight of what makes you happy and what brings you joy. You feel as if you've lost a part of who you are. How do you describe the loss and disconnection from yourself when you feel as if your life has been shattered? You collapse in a puddle of tears wanting nothing more than to be a mom. When you want something badly and feel the deep pull in your heart, you would do anything to make this dream of motherhood a reality. There's so much out of your control, and you feel at the mercy of your doctors and medical team. You want to be heard. You want some reassurance in the unknown.

The Pain that Bonds Us

Know that each feeling you experience is valid. Own your right to feel frustrated, sad, overwhelmed, and exhausted. It can be incredibly draining. Whether you're at the beginning of your journey or have had multiple failed cycles, the pain can become the center of your universe. It often takes over your life. Those who have never experienced fertility challenges don't fully understand. It can feel deeply lonely and isolating, as if you're the only one experiencing these feelings. Please know that you are not alone.

I remember the sadness and heartbreak when my husband and I realized we might have an uphill battle to face. I used my journal to stay positive and hopeful through it all despite feeling a lot of heartache. What good would it do for me to sit and wallow in complete despair? I chose to cling to hope and to trust that I was being guided. I wrote:

> *I have faith that things will happen the way they're*
> *meant to.*

I recall feelings of depression, which are pretty common for women struggling with fertility issues. I remember seeing others get pregnant so easily, and it brought on a pain that stripped away at my core. My husband and I didn't have any immediate friends (that we knew of) who were going through challenges getting pregnant, and I felt discouraged seeing others who were growing their families. I wondered, "*Why me?*" I questioned myself. I was tempted to question my worth, my purpose, and my value. I felt angry about the fact that I had worked so hard in my life and career, waiting to settle down and get married, only to be faced with fertility issues. I handled this pain through a lot of outlets. I found that writing helped, as well as getting outside to clear my head, talking with friends, and having many good cries. If anger, resentment, disbelief, or despair rise up, do not judge these feelings. Notice them. They want to be acknowledged. Start to become aware of these very real feelings and recognize their presence. They do serve a role in helping you move through this unknown territory.

The *Real* Pain of Infertility

These sentiments are shared by many. A fellow fertility sister describes the pain of IVF: *"Every day is a day we count with pain, sorrow, hope, and fear. This process is painful. Not the shots ... it's the emotional turmoil that is hard. You live by the calendar, counting down the days until you get to try again. Until you have another chance of being pregnant. Getting asked why you don't have kids yet. Watching everyone around you get pregnant while you stare at another negative pregnancy test in disbelief. Or get another bad phone call from the doctor's office.*"

She's right. The physical pain doesn't compare to the emotional pain of going through this process. It's a pain that goes right to your heart and soul. Add to that holding down a job with a boss who may be putting demands on you without knowing what you're going through. There's a lot of pressure to carry on as if everything is fine, when in reality we're on the verge of bursting into tears at any moment. Studies prove that the emotional stressors faced by women going through infertility are similar to those diagnosed with cancer.

You may feel like you're losing yourself. You may feel powerless in this process, thinking you have no control. I'm here to show you that you have more control than you realize. You can do hard things, and you can come out stronger than you ever thought possible.

There are no shortcuts on the path to motherhood, and sometimes you're faced with the need for fertility assistance. No one really sets out choosing this route, but if it's your current situation, I challenge you to consider seeing it through a new lens. It may be hard to imagine now, but I ask you to consider your fertility journey as one leading to a deepened discovery of yourself. This is a journey of your heart. It's one of possibilities. It's a journey within. Without a doubt, you'll be transformed forever.

I'm here to tell you there is a path through the darkness. There is hope.

Chapter 2

I've Got Your Back

"I have always thought of courage as the willingness to let the deepest longings of my soul grow larger than any fear that might arise."

—ORIAH MOUNTAIN DREAMER

DECIDING TO GO THROUGH IVF NOT ONLY TAKES COURAGE, it also takes accepting that you need assistance to start or grow your family. There are a variety of reasons you may be led to see a fertility specialist. Infertility is a medical diagnosis that affects both men and women. Male infertility issues could include low sperm count, poor motility, or poor shape, aka "morphology."

For women, infertility can result from a variety of reasons, including endometriosis, low ovarian reserve, blocked fallopian tubes, or a misshaped uterus. Although the reasons for infertility vary, they are deeply personal.

When my husband and I committed to going through this process, we approached it as a team. We longed for a child of our own and were ready to do whatever we could to make that dream a reality, together. Of course, when you start down this road, you are not handed a map to guide you to your destination. There's no instruction manual on what to do or how to go from point A to point B. You think it's going to be a straight line, but there are a million twists and turns that you don't expect and aren't always well equipped to deal with.

I feel that the rollercoaster of emotions is the biggest hurdle on this journey. Your mindset and the energy you bring to your IVF experience are key. Without having a manual on how to maneuver through the ups and downs of infertility, I went about our journey in the most intuitive way I knew. I had utmost faith, openness, trust, and hope. In recalling the way I navigated each step of this journey, I noticed some common themes emerge, which led to the book you are reading now. I saw a real need to create an instruction manual of sorts—a soulful guide on how to best navigate this crazy, emotional ride while optimizing your chances of success and not losing yourself along the way.

Before I share my story, my first recommendation for you is to throw your perceived timeline out the window. Having a timeline for your arrival at motherhood will not serve you. When you have expectations for how things should happen, and then they don't go according to plan, the stress and pressure can take over. This puts you at a disadvantage. It's rarely smooth sailing on this ride. You will likely encounter unexpected setbacks that will threaten to derail you, but don't for a minute think you are failing. Far from it. By beginning to let go of how you think it's supposed to go, you will be giving yourself one of the biggest gifts. Let go of the reins a bit and begin to get into a space of *allowing* instead of *forcing*. Please trust me when I tell you this. You may have *your* desired timeline, but the Universe will tell you otherwise. It will serve you well to begin to embrace the unknown.

Our Story

My husband and I met in 2012 and are a Match.com success story. I was in my mid-30s and he was in his early 40s. A Texas guy and a Colorado girl. We soon realized we were meant for each other. A year of dating, a year engaged, and a little over a year trying for a baby before we sought help. We began fertility testing in the fall of 2015. A friend, who also happened to be an OB-GYN and knew of our struggles, suggested we meet with a reproductive endocrinologist. We had a consultation and then started individual testing. Results indicated our chances of having a biological child naturally, without fertility assistance, were very low, approximately one percent. We not only learned I had uterine polyps that needed to be surgically removed, but we also learned we had male factor issues related to sperm. *"IVF is a definite possibility,"* they said. IUI was not a recommended option for us based on our issues. IVF would be our best shot, so we chose that route. Having a plan gave us some reassurance that we were on the right track. Since I would need to have a polypectomy early on in the process, we knew we would only be able to do a frozen embryo transfer at a later date, after my egg retrieval. A fresh embryo transfer was not in the cards for us.

I'll never forget when that big box of medications and needles for hormone injections arrived. My heart skips a beat remembering the start of it all, as I was trying to get a grasp on the adventure we had just begun. Our numbers in our first egg retrieval looked good, and we gathered four embryos. However, our joy quickly turned to heartbreak when we received the results from the pre-implantation genetic screening and learned that none of the embryos had matching chromosomes. I would likely have miscarried any of those embryos. A change-up to my protocol was advised, and I went through another round of abdominal injections for our second egg retrieval.

This time, we were able to get three embryos, with only one of those embryos being healthy with matching chromosomes. We had to freeze our little one as we proceeded with the recommended polyp surgery. The idea of having one potential child biologically linked to the two of us gave us so much hope. One embryo was holding on for us.

We had a year of surgeries, setbacks, and a lot more waiting ahead of us in 2016. The first surgery was having my uterine polyps removed. After three months of healing, we learned I had developed some scar tissue in my uterus. *Setback #1*: Our doctor informed us this scar tissue could affect implantation of the embryo, if it chose to implant there. I needed to have surgery to remove the scar tissue. When our surgery date was set, it just so happened to fall on our wedding anniversary. Not really the ideal way to celebrate our special day; however, nothing was more important to us than moving forward with the dream of growing our family.

I had the scar tissue removed and healing was going well. During this time, we prepared to proceed with our first embryo transfer. I had begun the medications. But then we encountered *Setback #2*. During a routine appointment, an ultrasound revealed a little bit of blood in my uterus, which caused the doctor to halt our proto-col and cancel the transfer. At this point, we were faced with the uncertainty of why this blood appeared. We were moving into the unknown, with more twists and turns. *Setback #3*: The first doctor overseeing our case had left the practice. What a time to face so much uncertainty without a clear plan in sight. All we knew was that we had one frozen embryo waiting for us.

During a consultation with Dr. Greene, my new doctor at the clinic, my husband and I inquired about next steps. He suggested having an ultrasound done to get some baseline data. Just when we thought we couldn't handle another setback, we had one. *Setback #4*: Fibroids had developed in my uterine lining and needed to be removed in order to give our one embryo the best shot at implantation. I was set up with an outside specialist to perform the fibroid removal. Thank goodness for all of these events happening, because the doctor also discovered some previously undetected endometriosis in my uterus. I healed for three months while we anxiously awaited receiving clearance to set a date for our frozen embryo transfer.

In January of 2017, literally three months from the date of my fibroid surgery, we had our first, and only, embryo transfer with our one embryo. *Our one held on for us.*

Witnessing our embryo being transferred into me was one of the most miraculous moments I've ever experienced. It's a vision in-grained in my memory forever. Holding hands with my husband in complete awe while the doctor zoomed in on the petri dish. My eyes couldn't believe what I saw. No more than a ball of cells. A dot (smaller than the size of the period at the end of this sentence) was placed inside me. I had a full bladder for the procedure, and I had to lay still for a short while. Talk about mind over matter when you have to pee like never before. I recall lying on the table realizing what had just transpired. We had a few minutes to ourselves, and I felt relief. We had made it. My husband buried his head in my arm, while tears started streaming down my face. Reaching this milestone was what my heart had been calling for. We had made it to this point but still had a long way to go. Our clinic gave us a picture of our embryo after it had been transferred into my womb. That image and another close-up image of our embryo are two of our most treasured keepsakes. They are a daily reminder of the miracle we witnessed that day. That little ball of light nestled into my womb, and we endured the two-week wait, in anticipation of hearing if we were pregnant. The call came. Eight months later, we welcomed our beautiful baby girl into the world.

Hold On, Baby, You Can Do This!

Although we can get so wrapped up in the physical aspects of this journey, I believe our pregnancy 'success' was a result of my soulful approach to the psychosocial and emotional challenges of IVF. That is why I wrote this book. Learning how to navigate the mental, emotional, and spiritual aspects of this journey is a crucial component of achieving success and keeping yourself together on this ride. It is the basis for my *IVF Soul Align Method*, which you'll learn more about in the next chapters of this book.

We cannot go through life without experiencing setbacks, challenges, disappointments, and struggles. That is where we grow. Our road was bumpy. After two egg retrievals and three unplanned surgeries, we found success with our one healthy embryo. We had just one shot of IVF working out. *Roll the dice, make a wish.* At the time of the initial draft of this book, our daughter was nearing her second birthday. She is nothing short of a miracle.

So I've got you, sister! I've lived this. I'm an effing fertility warrior, and so are you. I'm also an Occupational Therapist (OT) with a unique background in understanding the whole person. I know the value of using a holistic approach to maneuver through life's challenges. I take pride in the exclusive lens I used to help intuitively guide me through this process.

I felt supported and empowered as I walked through the maze of my fertility treatments, and I want to share this knowledge with you. In the next chapters, you will learn the strategies, practices, and supports I used to achieve success in my fertility journey, which is what I refer to as my *IVF Soul Align Method*. This book is a gift from my heart to yours. From one fertility sister to another. We share a bond that unites us, and I'm excited to shine the light for you to find your way through IVF and feel more grounded, hopeful, and inspired in the process.

Life doesn't happen to you; it happens for you.

As I trace the dots that have led me to where I am today, I'm filled with gratitude and struck with awe because I understand there are no accidents. I believe that everything that has happened *for* me so far in our fertility journey, and in life, has ultimately been for my growth. Of course, it is important to mention that we play key roles in our lives and challenging situations. We cannot be passive participants on our fertility path. We must be active participants in our IVF journey. It's essential.

What lessons can you begin to glean from the highs and lows you are experiencing on this path? We are responsible for the direction our lives go. We help steer the ship. I am here to tell you that *you have more control in this process than you realize*. The events that are happening in your fertility journey are there to help move you forward and guide you in the right direction.

Miracle Mindset

If there's any one secret to my getting through IVF successfully, I believe it was my mindset. I refer to it as a 'miracle mindset.' Are you using your thoughts and energy to your advantage as you navigate a path into the unknown?

I love that adopting this way of thinking makes life so much more fun and magical. The phrase *"Always expect something wonderful to happen"* resonates with me. Around the time my husband and I started fertility testing, I came across a beautiful art canvas with that saying on it. I bought it immediately. This is the mindset I've applied since my teen years, so I knew it was a mindset I had to use in my fertility journey, too.

Getting in the mindset where anything can happen and believing that miracles are everywhere requires openness, faith, and belief. There's an element of magic and mystery to it and a whole lot of fun. This way of thinking has led me to getting front row seats or meeting bands after concerts. I am familiar with getting rockstar parking quite often and opportunities to see and meet famous people, like Ellen and Oprah.

I carried the mindset of expecting good things to happen on our fertility journey. When you begin to understand how powerful your thoughts really are, you'll find a new secret weapon to aid you on your journey through IVF. You must adopt the mindset of a warrior. A warrior is ready to take on new challenges. A warrior carries an inner strength. Others may not see the battle scars you wear, but they'll feel your drive, your passion, and your heart. Each of us walking this IVF path is a warrior. Let's discover what it takes to build upon the inner strength of a warrior together.

Chapter 3

The *IVF Soul Align Method*

YOU MAY NOT FEEL LIKE A WARRIOR IN THIS MOMENT. I GET it. Perhaps you're feeling a bit defeated or even lost. There were times I felt this way too. And I worked through those feelings and made the choice to feel supported and guided through the IVF process. Through the next chapters in this book, I will invite and guide you to do the same.

Without a doubt, my 20-year career in occupational therapy informed me as I went through my own journey of IVF, and it helped me create the foundation for my *IVF Soul Align Method*. The primary focus in occupational therapy is taking a deep dive into what one wants and needs to do to live their best in life. Being an occupational therapist (OT) was of great assistance through this major life transition. I had to remember to live my life fully and not allow IVF to take over. I felt fortunate to have had a wide assortment of OT tools ready to use. I understood the importance of outside factors as well as factors within myself, knowing each had a role that influenced the way I would go through fertility treatments. This knowledge as an OT became one of my superpowers, and I'm excited to share how this unique background prepared me to apply these principles on the ride of infertility.

Being someone who was new to the world of infertility at the age of 38, I was reminded from my OT work experiences that many people have far greater challenges than what I was going through. My work at the time was focused on providing occupational therapy services to those receiving home health. Seeing the difficulties people deal with on an everyday basis helped put my fertility challenges in perspective. In home health, for example, a lot of individuals experience challenges with basic activities such as toileting, bathing, dressing, and grooming. Being able to get up and walk to the bathroom or engage in our favorite hobby is something many of us don't value until we cannot do it. When you encounter people dealing with everyday hardships, whether it be physical, cognitive, or developmental limitations, you are reminded that your challenges aren't nearly as big and insurmountable as you originally thought. You begin to focus on gratitude for what you *do* have and what you *can* do.

Helping others ignite the joy in their lives is another common area I focus on as an OT. I knew I needed to apply these same teachings while navigating the rocky road of IVF. It is vital to help my patients distinguish their problems from what's really important to them. Ask yourself what matters *to* you, not what's the matter *with* you. Knowing what matters to you will widen the lens on this journey. I'll be helping you discover the bigger picture of your fertility journey through my method of getting into soulful alignment.

Overview of the *IVF Soul Align Method*

Everything is interconnected—mind, body and spirit. Recognize that this is a holistic journey that can take its own sweet time. The wait may feel never-ending, but as I shared before, trying to control the timeline doesn't serve you. You will deepen your understanding of what patience really means.

Long before I tried to start a family, my friends lovingly nicknamed me 'Turtle.' Ironically, the turtle symbolizes my fertility journey quite well. I took the slow and steady path to become a mom. One step at a time. No hurry. Just movement forward. Perhaps you can relate to feeling flipped on your back with your feet up in the air. (Maybe you've even tried this post-sex as well!) There are times when we truly feel turned upside down and don't know what's up and what's down. This is what infertility does, and it can feel hard to put your neck out when you would rather hide in your shell.

Maybe you've tried everything to get pregnant, or you *think* you've tried everything. My hope is that the *IVF Soul Align Method* offers you a new perspective, a lifeline even, while you undergo IVF. Perhaps this process will serve you in other life challenges as well.

There is a way to get through IVF feeling more hopeful, more empowered, and more inspired. It's incredible looking back at the ways the Universe did conspire to support me through my IVF journey with grace and a sense of flow. I want you to experience this too. When I use the words Universe or God, I am referring to the same thing. You may call it Source, Spirit, Higher Power, or Highest Self. All are One. Use whatever word resonates with you.

The *IVF Soul Align Method* is centered around you getting soulfully-aligned with your desires. The next chapters in the book break down the process step by step. I recommend that you read the chapters in order, but if you're drawn to one of the chapters more than another, by all means, engage with the tools that resonate most with you.

As you read on, you will learn about the power of setting intentions and choosing a meaningful symbol to guide you toward your dreams. You will see how giving yourself permission to feel your emotions, releasing limiting beliefs, and navigating challenging setbacks will strengthen your inner warrior. You'll uncover the power of art and see how getting messy can be important self-care. Riding the ups and downs of IVF with the mindset of a warrior and surrounding yourself with a strong support system are key on this journey. I'll also guide you to further explore the benefit of tuning into your spiritual side. Your inner wisdom is waiting for you to crack her open and utilize her power. My *IVF Soul Align Method* is like no other. I'm sharing all my best tools, secrets, and strategies with you. These principles act as guideposts that can be applied not only to your fertility journey but also to your everyday life. There's really no separation. Let these principles become a way of life.

This wide assortment of tools will enhance your inner self discovery and lead you to uncover new practices that will help you align with your desires. I am here as your guide to enhance your ability to find success and achieve your desired outcome. I'm inviting you to see your journey as a gift, one of possibility. It takes beginning with an open heart and open mind to get in receiving mode. You will recognize the importance of mindset and how it can enhance your happiness and well-being while walking this path.

I want to invite you to begin with a practice that is foundational to the journey: journaling.

Power of Journaling

"If your life is worth living, it's worth recording."

—TONY ROBBINS

At the age of 10, my grandmother gave me my first journal. It was an old lock-and-key type book, which I dearly treasure to this day. Since then, I've kept many journals, which document the stories of my life. I am grateful that my grandmother inspired me to write about the feelings and events of my life. I still keep a journal, and it's a practice I will likely continue for the rest of my life.

During our fertility journey, I was journaling without knowing my entries would eventually become part of a book. Because I documented my journey, I am able to share many personal reflections from one of the hardest times of my life, in the hopes that they will bring you inspiration and hope. If you're riding the infertility rollercoaster, I have so much empathy for you. It might feel as if this ride will never end, and sometimes you're left to wonder when, if, or how to get off the rollercoaster. Only you will be able to answer that, but until then, I'm here to support you through the ups and downs.

At the end of each chapter, I will share key tips and journaling prompts to guide you on your path to motherhood. Journaling was a saving grace for me, and it will be an effective tool for you too. Treat yourself to a nice journal to accompany you on this adventure. Browse for one in a bookstore or online. Seek one that inspires you to fill its beautiful pages. You might prefer lined paper over unlined paper, or a bound instead of spiral journal. The choice is yours. You'll be amazed at what you'll learn about yourself and how therapeutic the act of putting pen to paper can be. Writing is powerful, and for me, it has been life-changing.

You are a badass fertility warrior. Repeat after me: *I am a badass fertility warrior.* I am writing to you, brave one. It's time to buckle up and embrace this ride of a lifetime.

Journaling Prompts

Open your new journal and begin to write about anything that comes to mind. Think of it as free flow writing.

- Let your pen flow and try not to think too much. Just look at this exercise as an introduction to some much-needed *you* time.

- Write about the pain you're feeling around infertility. Name it and declare it, and then write about it. Get it out of you and put it on paper. If you need to cry through your writing, then do it. Tears are healing.

- Write about the heartbreak you've experienced, but also start to think of your heart's desire. We'll be diving into this more in the next chapter.

Key Tips

Remember to give yourself credit for embarking on the path of IVF. You already are a warrior for stepping into the unknown. Life is happening *for* you, not *to* you. Be open to learning new approaches to support your body, mind, and spirit on this path.

Chapter 4

Set Your Intention, Seek Your Symbol

"I believe the choice to become a mother is the choice to become one of the greatest spiritual teachers there is."

—OPRAH WINFREY

I HAVE ALWAYS WANTED TO BE A MOM. IT WAS A DESIRE OF MY heart that I knew one day would come true. As I reflect on this dream I envisioned for myself, I can't help but think of my own mom. Motherhood ties in closely with our connection to our own mothers. We've all come from mothers. Whether or not we are close to our moms, we can thank them for bringing us into the world. Moms really are spiritual teachers. I know for certain my mom was, and still is, one of my greatest spiritual teachers.

Lessons From My Own Mom

As I remember my mom, I'm comforted by all the love she gave me and continues to give me. Those who knew her know just what an incredible person she was. At the time of writing this, I'm still less than one year out from the first anniversary of her passing. She and I shared such a close relationship, and I'm incredibly grateful for that. Working through grief takes time. It is difficult because of how much love I have for her. As you can imagine, this topic is deeply personal to me. I celebrate the woman who mothered me and who taught me how to be a mother. What a unique situation to have my own mom slipping away as I was striving to become a mother myself. I experienced the full cycle of life firsthand.

My mom's spiritual guidance continues on with the books she's given me and in the personal messages she inscribed. The last book she gave me was in June 2018, just two months before her passing. In it she wrote: *"How comforting to look within yourself and realize how we learn from the 'rough bumps' along the way. You bring hope and happiness to those you touch. I am so proud to be your mom. God's blessings to you always. Love, Mom."*

I remember speaking with one of the hospice nurses who shared with me that mom stayed up for most of the night trying to make that note to me just right. She seemed to struggle at times to express the exact meaning of what she wanted to say, but her message could not have been more perfect.

She helped me see that we grow most in life from the challenges we face and overcome. She and I had a great love for the book *Tuesdays with Morrie,* and we often talked about how life's little moments are actually the big moments. She showed me that there are times when life doesn't go according to plan, but it's how we react to hard things that counts. My mom made an effort to always tell me how much she loved me and how proud she was of me. As her health declined, we had even deeper conversations about life, living, and dying, and she wanted me to know that *"the love is always there."*

My mom's beliefs about life were shaped primarily by her father. I still feel my grandfather's presence in a special book that was his favorite, which became my mom's favorite and has now become a beloved book of mine: *The Prophet* by Kahlil Gibran. She gave me this book for Christmas in 2005. In it she inscribed: *"It gives many insights on life. Each time I re-read it, I learn something new. It has given me much comfort remembering how much my dad enjoyed it."*

In every written message to me, she would express how grateful she was to be my mom and that her love is with me always. These books are such a treasure for me in my grieving. I love that I can still connect with her through the pages of wisdom she left with me.

The desire to become a mom is not felt by everyone, but I know if you are reading this book you want this dream for yourself. Maybe you can relate to wanting to find the right partner before settling down and starting a family. Maybe your career was a priority and now you're ready to start a family. Maybe you're tired of waiting to find the right person and are going about it on your own. Whatever your situation, you are here now and may be considering which path to take to motherhood.

Isn't it funny how long we try *not* to get pregnant only to then want to hurry it up when we are ready? I used to think *"When I want a baby, I'll just be able to pop out a baby."* I thought it would happen easy breezy. Well, that wasn't quite the case, and I'm not alone. Thankfully, the conversation on this topic has opened up, with more and more people sharing their stories. The reality is that there's an increase in the number of women and men who are struggling to conceive. Are environmental factors to blame? Our diets? Technology? Stress? Age? Who really knows what's to blame, but whatever has led you to IVF, you are not alone.

Women are waiting longer. Careers are put at the forefront. People are waiting longer to get married and settle down. All of us have heard about the ticking biological clock. It is a very real thing, but we don't really like to focus on that. I remember hearing the term "geriatric pregnancy" for someone who is 35 or older. Who me? Thankfully, I didn't adopt these labels. Who even comes up with these ridiculous terms? If we're not careful, we start to believe them. We get into a bit of a panic. In our culture, we want things when we want them. Everything seems to move at a fast pace, and it's even harder when you're trying to rush a baby. As the years move on, we know our number of eggs declines too. We've learned that we're born with all the eggs we'll have. Throw advanced maternal age on top of that and it's a recipe none of us want any part of. We get scared hearing terms such as "low ovarian reserve." Thankfully, there are active things we can do to improve our numbers. Ultimately, we want hope.

I felt a lot of hope when I learned that IVF had a "definite possibility" of working out for us. We were, of course, scared about the unknown. I remember questioning the idea of how someone would scientifically try to make our baby, but I also believed technology had advanced enough to enable people like us to go this route. More advancements are being made in reproductive medicine every day. It just wasn't the path I'd envisioned for us, but we committed to it together and took it one day at a time. That's where you have to start. Whether starting down this road with a partner or by yourself, you have to get clear on your *why*. Set your intention. My first intention was to let my husband know we were in this together. We were going to be stronger because of this.

I journaled about my hopes and dreams at the start of our fertility testing. Here is a small excerpt from one of my journal entries:

It's all led to this moment. I'm happy. I'm content. Of course, I would like to make things happen to have a family. I want to make forward steps toward making my dream of having a family real. I can't imagine not being a mom and not having children. It's a passion of mine, and I cannot wait for that day. Life is good, and I'm moving forward in the right direction. All is well.

Set Your Intention

I know my success is a result of setting and writing clear intentions. It is helpful to get clear on your intention for why you want to become a mother. Consider your intention for your fertility journey as well. One of the intentions I set for myself at the beginning of our path was to *"find an inner peace that things will evolve just as they're meant to. Trust that things will work out."* I remember journaling about my intentions for why I wanted to become a mother. I was very aware that a child was not going to complete me. I had to feel complete within myself first. Coming from a place where you feel whole and filled up is easier said than done. It was a very emotional time.

I used journaling as a tool to help shed some of the emotional weight I was feeling. Writing in the affirmative that *'All is well'* really helped me in growing a strong foundation to support me on this unpredictable journey. I wrote about my desire to become a mom. I put forth the energy and desire of my heart that I would become a mom. Letting go of how it would all work out was key at this point. I knew I would reach my dream of motherhood in one way or another. If you have this dream to become a mother, I believe it can happen for you too. Maybe IVF is not the ultimate path to your baby, but you will find a way.

31

Writing out your intentions is the first important step in the *IVF Soul Alignment Method*. It is amazing to look back at my journals as well as some of the affirmation cards I created. One of them reads: *"I manifest great things coming my way. The right people will show up in my life to help me in accomplishing my dreams."* That they did.

One of the ways we can begin to loosen the reins of control on our fertility journey is to start opening up to the mindset that things are working out as they're meant to. I wholeheartedly believe this. It's pretty incredible what happens when you open yourself up to support from the Universe. It gives me chills realizing how well I was taken care of. Ask for guidance and be open to receive. The Universe wants to support us. It wants us to trust that we are being guided. When we want something badly, we often create more resistance to manifesting those desires into reality. Allow yourself the space to begin to let go. As hard as it may be, start to give yourself some grace and acknowledge the courageous person you are for stepping into the unfamiliar.

Journaling Prompts

- Take some time to get clear on your intention for *why* you want to become a mom.

- Journal about what you foresee this new role bringing to you.

- How will you *feel* once you become a mom or expand your family?

- Is there anything you're feeling afraid of?

- Write down any desires related to your own personal dream of motherhood.

- Do you have an intention for your fertility journey?

- How do you want to feel while on your path to motherhood?

Key Tips

The key is to let your pen flow. Whatever comes out is just what needs to come out. You may surprise yourself at what you discover while completing this exercise. Take 15 minutes or longer to write out your thoughts.

By getting clear on your intention, you are setting the stage for this process. You will gain clarity after this simple exercise.

The Power of a Symbol

Throughout the course of our IVF journey, I was given a few different, and very significant, symbols that supported me. Having something symbolic that I could physically hold during this process helped me immensely. The one that kicked off our IVF path was (and still is) very close to my heart. Maybe because it *is* a heart, the sweetest, most beautiful heart stone I have ever received. This heart was sent with a note from a dear family friend who wrote: " *This little heart's job is to protect you, to banish fears, and raise consciousness. Look at it in the light. Hold it close to you when you are resting and visualize a perfect outcome .... You are literally wrapped in the prayers and love from family and friends and always will be.* "

In time, I learned it's a labradorite stone, and even to this day, I feel a strong connection to it. It has given me profound healing during some of my most trying times. This stone is known to *'amplify the effects of healing prayers and affirmations, balance and protect the wearer, impart strength and perseverance, and is excellent for strengthening intuition.'* This stone gave me all of this and more.

A tangible symbol provides many benefits. A symbol is a reminder to stay connected to your intention. Look at it as a tool to help you anchor in the deep desires of your heart that are calling you to be a mom and grow your family. A deeply personal and meaningful symbol aids you, especially on those trying days. It helps ground you and brings you back to your center when you are feeling lost and disconnected on the IVF rollercoaster.

I suggest having something small enough to carry in your purse or pocket. You may have to search for your own symbol, or it may be gifted to you. In any case, I encourage you to stay open to receiving. When you are in that positive receiving state of mind, your symbol will arrive one way or another.

I also received another meaningful symbol that was a crocheted 'Hope' heart. It was sent from a friend and made by nuns at the hospital where she worked in New York City. Inside the sweet card, there was a quotation about hope: "*Of all the forces that make for a better world, none is more powerful than hope. With hope, one can think, one can work, one can dream. If you have hope, you have every-thing*" (Author Unknown).

I also received a gift of an amethyst bracelet with an angel wing attached to it. It read: "*Wear this bracelet always and you can discover the 'Art of Luck.' This Guardian Angel can protect you from evil, neg-ativity, and harm. Amethyst can fill your life with Good Health, Inner Beauty, and Inner Strength.*"

Symbols can show up in many forms, so enjoy the process of finding a symbol of your own. I can't tell you how much my heart symbol was a source of strength and hope when I was feeling low. The ener-gy I get from it is so comforting, like a warm hug or a gentle nudge when I need some added strength.

One fertility sister of mine shared that her symbol was a necklace with a mustard seed inside. When she needed inspiration during her fertility journey, she would look at this necklace. It reminded her that all she needed was the faith of a mustard seed. "*Sometimes that's all I had,*" she said. She wore it every day through the whole process, including her first pregnancy and miscarriage, and a second transfer and pregnancy with twins from a single embryo that split. About 20 weeks into her pregnancy, the mustard seed fell out, never to appear again. Losing this seed reminded her that she had the faith already. She knew it was inside of her all along, just like Dorothy's ruby slippers in *The Wizard of Oz*. Her twins are now almost two years old.

As we embark on our own personal paths to motherhood, we must remember our intentions for why we want to be mothers in the first place. Getting clear on your *why* helps direct the course of our fertility path. As you begin to feel more connected, grounded, and anchored to your deepest desires, you may find your symbol to support you. Sometimes these objects are meant to leave us, and sometimes they're meant to stay with us forever. Let it help guide you one step at a time down the path.

In my years post fertility challenges, I look to symbols as a source of strength, support, and continual guidance. Your symbol may even be a significant person in your life. My mom was certainly a symbol for me. The pages of this book are full of my mom's spirit and presence. Ever since her passing, I feel her constant support. Every day I wear her diamond stud earrings. She never took them off. Her wedding ring is another symbol I often wear, and it brings me comfort knowing how much her love lives on. What a gift when you uncover the symbols meant just for you.

Journaling Prompts

- Write about a special object that was given to you or that you found.

- Is it a source of comfort when you hold it? Is there another feeling you feel when you hold it? Remember, this is your symbol and how you define its meaning is personal.

- Is there someone in your life who acts as a guiding light for you? They just may be your symbol to hold on to.

Key Tips

If you don't have a symbol yet, have fun and be open to how your symbol will be revealed to you. Your symbol will help ground you and anchor you to your desires. You will find a lot of comfort and healing in your symbol. Look at is as a beacon of hope and a source of strength to guide you through the ups and downs.

Chapter 5

Don't Put Your Life on Hold

"Be bold enough to use your voice, brave enough to listen to your heart, and strong enough to live the life you've always imagined."

—UNKNOWN

GOING THROUGH INFERTILITY CHALLENGES CAN FEEL ALL-consuming. I get it. With all the doctor's appointments, scheduled injections, blood draws, ultrasounds, and tests, it feels as if your life is taken over by this process. Don't put your life on hold, though. Simple as that. You have a big life, and you have to continue living it. On your terms. I know how hard it is when you want something badly, and it becomes even harder when you want it to happen *now*.

Do What Makes You Happy

From the start of our infertility testing, I knew it was essential to continue living life despite the uncertainty that lay ahead. I was still seeing clients as an OT in rehab, skilled nursing, and home health settings, but I was also active in pursuing my leisure interests. Engaging in some physical activities, such as walking and workout classes, was a great outlet for me to channel my energy. Many of us have full-time jobs while going through our fertility challenges, and we don't always have the luxury of creating our own schedules. I had some flexibility with my work, but I was still juggling a lot. I wouldn't suggest taking on any big projects, but it is possible to get through, even if you have some big commitments in place. Staying active in pursuing interests and hobbies is a critical piece of navigating this ride. Keep your mind and heart stimulated and live life fully.

Look at what brings you joy. If cooking is your jam, I suggest getting back in the kitchen. Maybe you like to knit or crochet, or you're a reader. There are tons of different activities and hobbies to engage in. So often, I see women stop doing what once made them happy. If this is you, I encourage you to take a step back and reevaluate things. It's easy to become almost robotic in the formalities of the IVF process. Yes, we must follow the medication protocols we've been given by our reproductive endocrinologists. They are the "cooks in the kitchen," as my acupuncturist once said. They advise you on your medications and dosages, based on your personalized testing. They focus on your treatment plan. But I believe equally, if not more, in the need to focus on your emotional health and well-being. It is essential in this process. Helping you not lose yourself through this process is one of the biggest drivers for why I care so much and why I want to be a support to you on your fertility path. You must find and keep 'your happy.' Infertility does not deserve to be the primary driver in the car. Let it take the back seat.

Connect with Your Partner to Address Intimacy Challenges

If you are lucky to have someone by your side in this journey (such as a partner, wife, or husband), you must recognize infertility really does affect both of you. Having a date night now and again can keep the flame burning when it might feel like it's burnt out. During our infertility journey, my husband and I purchased a package of shows to the theatre. We still love going to the theatre and experiencing the arts with a night on the town. Going to shows can offer a way to escape for a short while from your current reality. Whether it's going to the theatre or a concert, I find these types of activities very therapeutic. Between the laughs and the tears, I'm always touched on an emotional level and often leave feeling more empowered and connected to myself and my husband. Dates with your significant other bring about new ways to connect and have some quality time, outside of fertility clinics and hospital rooms. Consider creative ways to take a step away from your current environment and treat yourself to a night out together.

It's a challenge to keep intimacy alive when trying to conceive. Infertility can appear to rob you of the joy you used to feel in the bedroom. Getting negative pregnancy tests each month can create added friction and a loss of interest in intimacy with your partner. If it becomes a bigger strain on you and your relationship than you imagined, I suggest seeking out counseling support. It's not easy to keep the romance burning when you're undergoing hormone treatments and your body and emotions are all out of sorts. The pressure for timed intercourse during your ovulation window doesn't create a lot of romance either. To keep the spark alive, my husband made me breakfast in bed, drew my baths, cooked dinner, or brought home a beautiful bouquet of flowers. The little things he did were often the big things for me (and they still are). Finding 'your happy' as a couple, and as an individual, is an important part of keeping yourself together on your way to parenthood.

Keep Shining your Light

Stay true to what lights you up. Looking back on the start of our fertility journey, I am flooded with memories of how joyful a time it was despite the challenges. I credit staying true to what lit me up as a tool to help get me through. I read inspiring books, attended some new Meetup groups, listened to powerful speakers, and participated in a book club. I met women who were taking bold action in their lives and taking ownership of their happiness. The energy I felt from these new people and places was contagious. One of my journal entries reads:

> *I'm thrilled to be surrounding myself with like-minded individuals who are growing and moving forward—that's what we're all here for. I've been recognizing the importance of being real, raw, vulnerable, accessible. It all takes real work, but what could be more valuable than getting to your truest, best self?*

It's amazing to look back at how everything on my journey was interconnected. I know this to be true for you too. You don't always know the reasons behind your desires, but they are waiting to be acknowledged and explored. One day during our IVF journey, I walked past a flyer for an event called the "Un-Job Fair." The title grabbed my attention, and I signed up to attend. At the event, I met a speaker named Barbara Winter. She wrote a special little book called *Making a Living Without a Job.* I know for certain I was meant to be there, meet her, and buy her book. Her wisdom is truly inspiring and her message ties into the soul of this book.

Listen to the Nudges

Listening to your heart's calling and tapping into your inner wisdom are paramount when enduring the ride of infertility. I'm so grateful to Barbara Winter for igniting the fire that has always burned within me to start my own business, lead with my passion, and use my natural gifts. I truly believe that first step of saying yes and attending that fair helped launch me down a path I could never have planned on my own. During this journey, be open to magical encounters. The people and guides who cross your path may open doors that lead to something amazing you can't begin to see right now. You will be rewarded when you trust the unknown and take that step forward, even if it feels a bit out of your comfort zone.

Elizabeth Gilbert explains in her book *Big Magic* to follow the bread-crumbs. When you open yourself up, the right support will begin to show up. It's as if you're being led down the path exactly meant for you. This became very true for me while going through IVF.

How do you begin to hear the nudges? Well, it requires you to get very quiet within. You must tap into the mode of receiving, and ask yourself what is calling you. It takes being curious.

Looking back on my life as a young girl, I remember a piece of art that hung in my bedroom, framed in light blue. On it was a picture of a young boy holding up a shell to a young girl's ear. They were standing on the beach with the ocean waves crashing behind them. This was a gift from my mom. One day, I'll pass on this keepsake to my daughter in tribute to my mom. It reads:

Listening
to your heart,
finding out who you are,
is not simple.

43

It takes time for
The chatter to quiet down.
In the silence of 'not doing'
We begin to know
What we feel.
If we listen and hear
What is being offered,
Then anything in life
Can be our guide.
Listen.
—Anonymous

Say Yes to Something New

When you begin to listen to the nudges, you feel more alive and lit up inside. Sometimes you just can't ignore the calling, and you have to awaken to the deeper pulls within. As you listen and notice, you begin to realize the Universe is communicating with you all the time. It's ready and willing to help us move in the direction that serve our highest selves. You're led to a new path, out of stagnation, out of a rut, and you are more turned on inside. By pursuing the dreams of your heart in all aspects of your life—including work, play and self-care—you become a magnet for new energy to flow. The bottom line is to say *yes* to your big, bold life and know that there is so much untapped potential energy waiting for you.

But how does this all tie into becoming a mother? I believe your future baby desires a mama who is living life fully, even with all the ups and downs. It's all a part of life. We have to ride the waves, and we can do this with flow and ease. When you answer the call within, you get more connected with the spirit of your baby-to-be.

One of the most significant steps I made was joining my first book club called the Real Life Book Club. What I loved most about this group was that it attracted women seeking personal growth. All of the books were focused on the theme of personal growth and development. I waited for that nudge to speak to me on which book I felt called to read and which leader felt most aligned with me at the time. The first book I signed up for was *Playing Big* by Tara Mohr. Here I was in this space of desiring to become a mom, pursuing the route of IVF. I was welcoming new, inspired ideas, and I was eager to *play big*. This book kicked things into high gear for me. After I read it, everything started shifting in major ways, giving me momentum and joy and also bringing in the support I needed on my path to motherhood. I felt lit up and alive inside. I was taking ownership of my own joy and happiness, while also surrounding myself with a sisterhood of women who were there to lift me up in some of my lowest moments. If I had tried searching for this kind of group, it would not have been nearly as magical as the way it all came to me. The social events I also attended enabled me to connect with other women who became invaluable supports to me on my fertility journey. The heart is often the best compass in helping us know where to go.

I also knew I was on the right path when I had the opportunity to attend a retreat called the Fearless Female Summit in Denver. Lisa Nichols was the guest speaker. I knew I had to be there. My journal pages were full of scribbles of the wisdom Lisa was sharing. I had been a fan of hers for years after discovering her in the movie, *The Secret*. At the end of the day's event, she spent time connecting with us individually. I shared my infertility story and how I was now 10 weeks pregnant. Without hesitation, she held me and asked if she could send some prayers. She lovingly placed her hands on my womb, sending prayers and love to our sweet one. In that moment, I knew in my heart I was right where I was meant to be. It was all unfolding in the absolute best way possible.

By listening to those nudges, we tap into a new energy. Magical things can and will unfold when we step into this new space. It's when you step out of your comfort zone that things really do start shifting and lining up for you. I encourage you to try something new.

There were so many positive things in my life because I chose not to put my life on hold. The personal development work I was doing was important to me and was helping me get to where I wanted to be. Reading through my journals, I noticed how at peace I felt.

> *Everything that is happening in my life right now is the way it's supposed to be ... joining the Book Club, meeting these ladies, taking a break from (full-time) work and rediscovering my passions. Focusing on where I want to spend my time.*

I could feel an energy shifting in me. The day of this journal entry I had ordered Brené Brown tickets to hear her speak in Denver about her latest book, *Rising Strong*. It all felt aligned and reassured me I was right where I needed to be.

Living our lives every day takes trust. Whether it's trust to explore something new or the trust we put in our medical providers as we embark into the unknown world of IVF, we're faced with the choice to trust. I wrote in my journal:

> **Trust**. *Things will work out.*

Journaling Prompts

- Identify one calling that's nudging you. What are you curious about?

- What are you feeling called to try?

- What's holding you back from taking action?

- Write about one step you can take to move yourself forward.

- What kinds of activities do you love to do? Look at what you used to do and have stopped doing since going through infertility.

- Free flow and write all the joys you remember as a child.

- Dream up fun activities for you and your partner to try—maybe a cooking class or a weekend getaway to a new place.

Key Tips

It takes courage to listen to your inner whispers, to pay attention to them and act on them. They are there to guide you. Don't ignore them. Don't put your life on hold. Keep moving forward. You just never know what opportunities may unfold for you. They may just be the breakthrough you need to help you get through any breakdowns you may be facing. Get quiet and find your happy within. Keep the spark alive between you and your partner, and consider the impact your infertility challenges may be having on your significant other. Approach this journey as a team, and you'll be that much stronger.

Chapter 6

Let It Go

"Life is a balance of holding on and letting go."

—RUMI

IT WAS AUGUST OF 2016 WHEN I WAS TOLD DURING A ROUTINE ultrasound that I had some blood in my uterus, and we were going to have to cancel the upcoming embryo transfer.

When going through IVF, you come up against many obstacles. Surprisingly, I can tell you now that this blood may have been the biggest blessing. But at the time, hearing that the procedure was cancelled really stung at the time. It seemed like we were experiencing one setback after another. We were just weeks away from our first scheduled embryo transfer in September of 2016, and the Universe said, *"Nope. Not yet."* Let me take you back to the start of it all to give you an idea of the road we had been on up to this point. Maybe you've had a similar path.

We were about a year into our fertility journey and had gone through two egg retrievals to get one healthy embryo. That one was frozen as we proceeded to the next stage. Early on, I learned I had polyps in my uterus that had to be removed. My first doctor suggested banking more embryos, to have more potential opportunities to conceive, but we chose not to and kept faith that our one would work. Call it naïve maybe, but my husband and I felt called to keep moving forward.

The polypectomy was next—byebye polyps. After three months of healing, I had another ultrasound, and the doctor found scar tissue inside my uterus from the polyp surgery and suggested I have it removed. She said, *"You have one embryo, and if the embryo decides to implant there, it may pose problems."* In no way did I want to take that chance, so we accepted that we would have to wait a bit longer. I appreciated that my doctor was cognizant of the fact that we only had one embryo. They were doing everything they could to optimize our chances of this working out.

Fast forward to having surgery to remove the scar tissue. This surgery just so happened to occur on our wedding anniversary. Happy second anniversary to us! Lots had been happening up to this point. Just two months prior, we had moved into our new home, in a new part of town, which happened to occur on my birthday, of all days! At this time, my husband had also started a new job. Some big life transitions were happening. I've learned it is best to develop the skill of adaptability when so many changes are happening simultaneously.

> *I'm thankful we're getting closer to our goals. For a while I had a lot of dreams about the embryo transfer ... now I'm focusing more on surrendering ... on letting go.*

This time of transition became a pivotal point for me, as you can see from the journal entry above. I felt the best thing I could do was simply to ride the wave, to let go of what I couldn't control, and focus on what I *could* control. You will feel freer on this path when you choose to let go. We don't know how long the ride of infertility will last, or where exactly it's going to take us, but with so much unknown, it's helpful to focus on practices that bring you joy. It is crucial to amplify your well-being above all else. And that is something you do have control over.

One of the ways I enhanced my sense of joy and well-being was through reaching out to friends for extra support. My friend Amanda shared some of her expertise with a visualization for increasing our fertility. I applied her teachings by sending positive thoughts and healing energy to myself and my body. Below is one of the powerful practices I did, and here are her exact instructions to me.

The Honey Pot Practice:

Make a triangle with your hands, with your thumbs touching and your pointer fingers touching. Place them over your pelvic area, right below your belly button. Then, you will bring a smile to your face, and breathe in deeply. Imagine this area is a beautiful pot of sticky, delicious honey. Imagine you are filling the honey pot with love and whatever other intentions you have: fertility, vitality, etc. Then you will imagine the honey is dripping all over your pelvis, all over your lady parts, and going up your vaginal canal into your cervix, uterus, fallopian tubes, ovaries, everywhere, sending love and your intention. Keep your focus in your body, sending love there. Lots of love. Then just gently shake your pelvis with your hands still in the triangle, sending love, and take a closing breath, and you are done.

I invite you to try the above visualization. You have this power. I learned early on that I would do whatever I could to nurture myself and stay open-minded while on this path. Knowing that everything is energy, I wanted to embody this way of thinking. It could only help me.

Riding the Ups and Downs in Life

While waiting to see how my body would heal from the scar tissue surgery, I was overwhelmed with the unknown at times. I was beginning to sink into deeper sadness as I watched my mom's health continue to decline. I allowed myself to cry, like *really* cry. I poured my heart out, thinking how much I wanted to be a mom. How much I wanted my mother to meet her only grandchild. How much I wanted her to be here to witness the day of me becoming a mom. Writing was a therapeutic outlet for me, and I wrote a lot about my mom. One of my entries helped me in looking at my mom's challenges—up close and personal.

> *I see your struggles; I see your discomfort. I see you make the best of your situation with a smile on your face. I don't think anyone knows what you go through on a daily basis.*
>
> *The coughing, the challenge of just breathing.*

The simple act of breathing was one of her biggest struggles, and it's something we all take for granted. She had real fears of losing her breath and running out of oxygen. I can remember seeing the fear in her face. It literally brings tears to my eyes as I write this because she handled her fears the best way she knew how, with a grace I so admire. Her attitude toward her condition inspired me immensely.

One of my mom's lasting gifts is her ability to help me see the bigger picture. Yes, infertility was hard, but I could choose how I looked at it. At a time when I had all the obstacles of IVF in front of me, I looked to her as a model on how to help me get through it. She showed me that challenges would always appear in life, but we do not have to let them consume us. My mom didn't dwell on her limitations, and I knew I couldn't either. I chose to push through my limiting beliefs just like my mom did. Seeing her health decline, I was exposed to the fragility of life in a way I hadn't experienced before.

Love Letters

I wrote a lot about my mom during this period of uncertainty. I believe in the power of physically writing out our desires, our pains, and our dreams. Whenever I'm feeling lost, I know I can find some release in the act of putting pen to paper. There's something about moving what's *inside* us to a place *outside* of us, in the physical form. It seems more tangible to hold.

During this time, I also began writing love letters to our embryo. I found an intense pull to write often, and I followed my instincts to start the practice of letter writing. It was a way for me to turn my pain into a heartfelt call to our baby's spirit. Whenever I physically hold the letters I wrote to our baby, it's quite magical. I knew our future baby would get a sense of just how much they were loved and almost *willed* to be here. The intention behind my letters was for the spirit of them to be received. I encourage you to give it a try. You can start by taking a few minutes to center yourself before you begin writing. I found it helpful to be in a space of silence and solitude when I wrote to our sweet one. When you're ready, either type or hand write whatever comes from the heart. I wouldn't edit too much, just let the *energy* of your words flow through you. Think of it like poetry. It doesn't have to have rhyme or reason. It is best expressed from the deep longings of your heart. You might find you are restored and replenished by this exercise. It's a gift for your sweet baby-to-be and also a gift for you.

Treat Yourself

Taking time to give yourself some TLC helps when you're struggling to keep it all together. I sought out joyful experiences as much as I could. Every once in a while, I would treat myself to a massage or get a manicure or pedicure. I also found relief in doing healing treatments of acupuncture and Reiki. Both of these practices supported me by keeping me in a more balanced state. I could feel the healing and nourishment on a deep, energetic level. The acupuncture and the Reiki energy kept me aligned. These holistic practices comforted me and allowed me to talk through fears, while relaxing deeply.

Other indulgences were savoring an occasional small glass of wine and allowing myself a favorite coffee drink now and then. I believe you should not completely deprive yourself of things that bring you joy. Of course, consult your doctor for recommendations on what to avoid, but ultimately, do what feels right to you. I felt little treats were necessary for all I was going through with fertility treatments and procedures. It gave my soul a boost to treat myself by attending speaking events with girlfriends and going to a one-day yoga conference. Listen to what feeds your inner fire. Taking walks, being in nature, enjoying my favorite music, reading a good book—all of these things refueled me. During my months of recovering from my surgeries, I made it a priority to live with a positive, conscious mindset focused on healing. A journal entry of mine focused on my intention and my truth.

> *My intention is to feel a light inside, a warmth and peace that everything is going to be alright. I have so much love, support, and prayers. The Universe has my back and is doing everything to work in my favor. So many people are rooting for us—I feel the love and energy.*

Learning from Waiting and Setbacks

You will inevitably find yourself playing the waiting game during the IVF journey, so it's important to find ways to make the waiting more fun. In my case, while taking the injections in preparation for our upcoming transfer, I felt empowered to connect with a photographer friend to take some professional photos of me so that she could capture my experiences during this process. You might think I was crazy to have pictures taken, but as I look at them now, I see strength. I'm holding my belly, looking up at the sky, holding my journal, holding my heart symbol, and sitting in quiet reflection. There is so much to celebrate in those photos. I was finding *joy in the journey*. Whenever I look at these photos, I see a woman who is resilient and faithful despite the obstacles she was facing. She was in a state of preparation, getting ready to mother her baby-to-be.

This is *you*. Remember you are strong. You are resilient. Your setbacks are there to guide you in the right direction. Even though I was waiting, I took time to celebrate the journey along the way. I encourage you to celebrate this period of your life too. One of the covers of my journal reads:

> *It may not be easy, but it will be worth it.*

I became passionate about starting my blog, and I knew that I had a lot to share with others on this path. I know it is no coincidence that as I was deep into my pursuit to birth a baby, I was also birthing new creativity. New ideas were coming to me.

With each setback, I grew even stronger. Just days away from our transfer, we got the news about blood in my uterus. With a cancelled embryo transfer, we were feeling lost. Yet we were still hopeful that our embryo was waiting for us. As if we didn't have enough stress going on, this is also when we learned that the original doctor assigned to our case was leaving the practice. We had to keep pressing onward. *Hold on, baby! We are coming for you.*

It was a good thing we had built up our resilience muscles, because we were thrown yet another setback when our new doctor discovered I had fibroids in my uterine lining that needed to be removed. I was told I had at least three of them and one was the size of an orange. The fibroids in my uterine lining posed a problem if our embryo decided to implant there. Another surgery was scheduled.

I was referred out for fibroid surgery, and that doctor discovered and removed six fibroids and some endometriosis. The recovery from this surgery wasn't easy, but eventually I began to feel better and was soon on the road to healing.

Setbacks in life are inevitable. We can choose to accept them, or we can choose to resist them. Of course, letting yourself be sad is more than okay and actually very healing. You have to feel to heal.

Maybe your setback involves seeing others who seem to easily get pregnant with their second or third child. I felt the sting of these feelings too. I let myself work through these emotions by feeling them, writing about them, and talking it out with friends. Pouring out our emotions is healthy. I recall writing how sad, angry, and jealous I was. My eyes became tired and weak from crying so hard. Take the time to scribble out any undesirable feelings you may be having. Allow yourself the opportunity to again acknowledge their presence, and then set them free. Setbacks will happen, and often they are out of our control. The key is to find a way to *release* in some way.

Keep Stress to a Minimum

Infertility is inherently stressful, but you do have control on how many additional stressors you invite into your life. It's easier said than done, right? We have all heard the unsolicited advice 'just relax and you'll get pregnant,' which is not helpful. If all I had to do was just relax to have a baby, then just imagine how much money, time, tears, and pain we would have saved!

You may not be able to fully relax, but you can take ownership of what you decide to take on and what you choose to let go. I made the mistake of taking on a really big project in the months leading up to our fertility challenges. I volunteered to be the conference chair for our state occupational therapy association's annual conference. The role was demanding, yet I stayed committed to fulfilling my professional responsibilities regarding the conference, which unfortunately was at an already stressful time for me. The added stress took its toll.

Yet there were silver linings that kept my spirits high. Right before my mother's passing, I found a journal I had given to her years before as a Christmas gift. I had asked her to fill it with personal stories, insights, and reflections that she could one day give back to me. When I opened it up, there was only one journal entry, and it was four pages long. It was perfect, and one of the most loving gifts I have from my mom. It was dated on my 21st birthday. Her words have helped me through some of my darkest moments. This was an excerpt I read aloud when I gave her eulogy:

> *If there is one thought I would share, it's that it's not what happens to you in your life—it's how you deal with it. You have a lot of inner strength—use that to guide you. Take responsibility for your own life. No one can do to you what you won't let them. Be open to learning from each new experience. Life is full of change, growth, and new insights.*

My mother instilled in me an inner strength and an inner knowledge that I would be guided in life. I could trust I was on the right path. Embracing change, growing, and learning from our setbacks are forms of timeless wisdom that will carry us through the ups and downs of this journey.

Journaling Prompts

• Write about a perceived setback you've experienced that has opened the door into something even better.

• Are there setbacks you're presently facing in your IVF journey? Take 10 minutes or so to let your pen flow and put them on paper.

• Can you begin to see how this setback could possibly have a silver lining you may not be aware of yet?

Key Tips

When we learn to let go in our lives, we set ourselves free. There will be obstacles you'll encounter on the IVF path, but I challenge you to see them as a guide for getting you to where you need to be. Our obstacles aren't intended to cause us more pain. Yes, you need to feel the pain, but then be ready to choose the path forward. Allow yourself to grieve your losses, and take as much time as you need. As badly as we want something right now, remember that there is a divine order to it all. Learn to ride the wave.

Chapter 7

Let It Out

"Never apologize for being sensitive or emotional. It's a sign that you have a big heart and that you aren't afraid to let others see it. Showing your emotions is a sign of strength."

—BRIGITTE NICOLE

"I'M REALLY SORRY, BUT NONE OF YOUR FOUR EMBRYOS CAME BACK HEALTHY AFTER TESTING." Hearing these words in January of 2016 was such a heartbreaking setback.

I was devastated and in shock, and, eventually, I couldn't hold it in anymore. I was overcome with emotion, tears running down my face. I was at my clinic check-in counter getting ready to prepare for an upcoming procedure when I got the news. The timing could not have been worse. I can't even remember what I told my husband, but he drove to meet me as quickly as he could. My body collapsed into his arms. I had never experienced a heartbreak like this. We held each other while feeling all the heavy emotions of loss. To say we were overwhelmed is an understatement. We allowed ourselves to cry and grieve the loss of our four embryos. Just weeks before, I had wrapped a special Christmas present for my husband. The look on his face when he saw the pictures of our embryos completely warmed my heart. He was on his way to becoming a daddy, but now that dream was stripped away.

I felt a deep sadness that was probably one of the lowest times I had ever experienced thus far on our journey. It was hard not to feel utter disappointment and discouragement after going through a whole round of hormone injections, multiple blood draws, and ultrasound checks, as well as dealing with all of the side effects of the hormones that had been pumped into me. It just felt like a total loss—all the time, the hoping, and the money that had gone into this, all the medications and appointments. It seemed hard to imagine starting all over again. The pain surrounding infertility challenges goes right to the root of us. Know you are not alone in this heartbreak.

Feel It Out

What can you do to help ease this pain? The place to start is to let yourself *feel* the emotions that come up for you. Feeling is healthy and necessary. I don't encourage you to hold these feelings in or stuff these feelings down, as they will only fester and become bigger challenges as you continue on this path. Sit with your emotions. Cry for as long as you need to. Yell, scream, punch, or kick (preferably a pillow or boxing bag). It's important to *release* these emotions. Let them pour out of you.

If you're angry, feel that. Sad? Feel it. Get it out. Don't let it swell and take up space in you. Release it so you can shift this energy and feel freer. Give yourself permission to fully feel and by doing this, you'll find greater peace and joy within.

Emotion = Energy in Motion

Emotions are connected to the core of who we are, the center of creation. If we're holding onto emotions, we are also tightening up the space in our womb area. We begin to heal this space by *feeling our emotions* and then letting it all out. I didn't want anything to do with feeling heavy. Crying and writing were ways I released and felt lighter.

You can also take a towel or pillow and scream into it from the pit of your belly, from the depth of your lungs. *Let it out.* This really can be a transformative exercise that helps you create more space within. It allows the old emotions to come out, so you can feel renewed again. You are then able to let the magic come back in. When you are done releasing, you will feel a sense of freedom, and you can begin to bring in the light.

Other issues may begin to appear in our bodies if we don't let out these hard feelings. We may find ourselves with more headaches, irritable belly aches, back pain, and so forth. It's essential to first recognize what we're feeling. By acknowledging the feelings first, we can then assign emotions to them and begin the process of releasing.

Seeing My Mom's Decline

In the summer of 2016, my husband and I were in a long waiting period. I had undergone two surgeries at this point before scheduling our embryo transfer. During this trying time of surgeries and dealing with our infertility challenges, I was also consumed by the fear of losing my mom. In July of that year, I had a moment that it really hit me. My husband helped me recognize that my mom needed a break. She had been dealing with her respiratory condition for so long and was truly tired. That night, as I cried my eyes out,

I wrote:

>*It was a gift in a way, to help me cope and gain perspective.*

I had become aware that her stamina had significantly decreased, and her breathing became more labored with very simple movements. I let the tears fall.

>*I see a change in my mom. One that scares me. I see her slowing down. I can't write the word.*

I didn't want to face the fact that my mom was dying.

I found a lot of comfort in writing in my journal to help me process what I was feeling. I noted conversations I had with my mom that, although very sad, brought me a lot of comfort. Hearing her say I was meant to be her daughter, and she was meant to be my mom, was such a gift. We had many of those really hard conversations, and I look back with appreciation that we both could be vulnerable and share what we felt from the heart. There were a lot of tears. The phrase she said that will never leave me is *"Love is forever. It's always with us. The love is always there."* My hope is these words resonate with you on some level. When you're grieving your losses, and unsure of how you will stay afloat, be reminded of these words. You are never alone. Love is always there.

I wrote the following poem about my mom on the night I had released all my tears.

My mom—
Special light in my life.
She guides me,
Teaches me,
But most important,
Loves me.
Her strength,
Her persistence and
Dedication to
Keeping a positive attitude,
And to make the best of her situation.
She inspires me more
Than she may ever know,
And I want her to know that.
I feel a connection
To her maybe more than
Ever ... I want the work I do
To be a reflection of her and the role,
The influence she has had on my life. I'm
Her daughter and I want her light to shine
Through me.

Journaling Prompts

Think of the emotions you are feeling that may be weighing you down. Set a timer for 10 minutes and write whatever comes to mind. Where can you begin to release and start to feel a bit lighter?

- Give yourself permission to fully feel. Imagine releasing it all out of you. You may try the exercise of yelling into a towel or pillow. Honor the space to let it out. Empty these emotions that you may be suppressing. Little by little, you'll notice how things begin to open up for you.

- Think of someone in your life who you admire, who has the attitude of a warrior. In what ways do they inspire you to live bolder and braver?

- If you feel inspired, consider writing a heartfelt poem or letter—maybe it's about someone else, or maybe it's about *you*. It just may be the love letter your soul is calling for.

Key Tips

Do whatever you need to do to help move the heavy emotions out so you can experience more freedom and joy. Feel the highs and the lows, and push yourself to experience these edges. This is where expansion happens. My dear friend Lisseth was instrumental in helping me learn the edges are where we grow. Think of your emotions as little messengers supporting you and delivering important information, as you ride the ups and downs of infertility. Get comfortable being uncomfortable, and you'll find a new freedom. I invite you to welcome the emotions that arise on this journey. Don't push them aside, but rather *feel* them and *release* them. You will begin to find freedom when you let go.

Chapter 8

Get Messy:
The Healing Power of Art

"Man, through the use of his hands, as they are energized by mind and will, can influence the state of his own health."

—MARY REILY, OTR, EDD

THE IDEA OF CONCEPTION IS DEEPLY INTERTWINED WITH the creative process. We are creating our lives every single day, every moment of every day, and it's no different when you're trying to conceive. It is an act of creation. We are *creating life*. Whether we have Assisted Reproductive Technology to help us grow our family or we create the old-fashioned way, it's truly miraculous that it just takes one egg and one sperm to create a human being.

When you're on the path of trying to create a new little person, I challenge you to pause and consider bringing out your own inner kid. Picture yourself in your younger years. Do you remember the joy of engaging in crafts as a kid and getting your hands dirty? Do you remember looking at a blank sheet of paper and envisioning what you would draw, color, or finger-paint? Do you remember the smell of Play-Doh and how it feels to mold it in your hands? Think of the last time you did something creative.

Engaging in art, or any creative activity where you can unleash your inner kid, supports you while going through fertility challenges. You may find a new sense of freedom and relief as you use your hands to release tension that may be hiding inside of you. I want to ignite a love of creative expression which will kick-start you into a state of joy. You'll find it very therapeutic when you get your hands engaged in a craft or task. I found a new freedom when I put a paintbrush to canvas.

Art Smash

Early on in my family's fertility journey, I met a woman who invited me to be a beta tester in a program she created called "Art Smash." I knew art was healing, and I knew it would be the best kind of medicine to support me and my mental health as the rollercoaster of emotions was ramping up.

For one of the first exercises, I was asked to visualize and write about the opening scene of a movie. *My* movie. I had to get clear on what I wanted to draw into my life. What did I want to manifest? One thing I wanted to bring into my reality was a warm home that was cozy and inviting. In addition to undergoing fertility treatments, my husband and I were also house hunting. (Only to add a little more stress on top of it all, right?) Other visions in my opening scene included getting pregnant, having a belly, and having children. I also wanted to start a regular meditative practice to help get in a clear headspace. A focus on exercise and fueling my body and mind with healthy food were other wishes. I understood the interconnectedness of nurturing myself in order to nurture my future babies.

As I began my first attempt at painting, my art was reflecting back my reality. The instructor could sense my frustration with what I'd painted and asked me to *"paint something which gives a visceral feeling."* I chose black and completely marked out the painting I did. I chose to let go of perfection and decided to use my creative power to go bolder, and then I drew a heart in red. Behind it were the black strokes, but the heart still showed above them. I journaled:

> *My heart is still at the center of this mess.*

The heart was in color which made me think of it still having life, a heartbeat. I had hope. The instructor noticed a 'protection' around the heart. I definitely felt that way and think that anyone going through fertility challenges can relate. We want to protect what's sacred to us. We may be open to sharing with a few select friends about our path to motherhood, but then with others we may feel the need to guard and protect. We protect because becoming a mother is likely one of the deepest hopes and dreams that we experience in this lifetime. To bring life into this world. To be called *mother.* I wanted this more than anything.

When you go through losing embryos, you feel completely heart-broken. When I started this art program, my husband and I were at a pivotal point. We knew we weren't going to stop. We wanted to try again and keep moving forward. The emotions around that time are still fresh, as I recall painting that dark color of protection around the heart.

My hopes and dreams are focused on starting a family, and I do have a strong protective layer around that. How could I not? Human life .... We had four embryos and now are having to begin again in the hopes it will work out for us.

When you're on this journey, you understand how precious life is, and in this case, *new* life. Having the assistance of advanced reproductive technology will never dampen my faith in miracles. Consider what a gift it is to have this technology available today. It is an art form. I give so much praise to the medical professionals who have mastered this art and continue to refine it. A painter creates through paintings. An embryologist helps create "em-babies." My husband and I created *our* baby. This incredible science will forever astound me.

Art Is Healing

The art program became a lifeline for me in helping me *hold on* to myself. I recall feeling very overwhelmed with the loss of our embryos and the idea of starting a round of medications all over again, but, thankfully, art became a true gift.

When we engage in art, let go of control, and allow ourselves to be in the mess, we open ourselves up to new energy, new creativity, and a sense of freedom. The instructor asked me to consider the question, *"What is so awful about letting go of control?"* There's so much that came up around this topic, but it all helped me adopt the mindset of letting go. There is immense power when we let our logical brains sit back and get out of the comfort zone.

The miraculous thing about getting messy in the experience of creating art is that when you're in it, you really don't want to get out of it. It's where the magic happens. Yes. *The magic is in the mess.*

Art Comes in All Forms

As I think back to the clients I've worked with in skilled nursing and rehabilitation facilities, I'm reminded how much people crave the opportunity to let their creativity shine. Put yourself in the place of an 85-year-old woman who used to play the piano. Her arthritic hands hadn't touched a piano in some time, but when she was presented with a piano, her face lit up and her fingers danced across the keys and renewed her sense of joy.

In one group session, we provided a chance for older individuals to do some gardening and plant flowers. My clients' faces lit up with pleasure as they got their hands dirty. They loved the feeling of the dirt in their hands, the sunshine on their faces, and the wonderful aromas in the air. This activity gave some life back to them and restored a sense of well-being. Try to imagine how depleted you might feel without the opportunity to engage in your favorite hobbies. Engaging in meaningful and creative activities while undergoing fertility treatments will help restore your beautifully broken soul.

One of my clients had a diagnosis of Guillain-Barré. This autoimmune disorder caused a lot of pain, numbness, and weakness in her hands. We explored various sensory interventions and discovered that cooking was one activity she could do with only minimal discomfort. During a therapy session, we rolled dough with our hands to make cookies, and she was over the moon excited to use her hands again with this purposeful therapeutic activity.

The power of music and dancing is also deeply therapeutic. My

71

clients always had a spark in their eyes when their favorite music was on. Those with cognitive impairment such as Alzheimer's disease showed a positive response to these types of creative activities. When we're engaged in the arts, we come alive. Our senses wake up. We're renewed.

One of my favorite clients was a gentleman who used to be a George Burns impersonator. I learned he used to do shows in Las Vegas. His spirit had been dampened by some physical limitations in his older age. When I suggested the idea of him doing a show for the other residents in the facility, he laughed it off at first. When he knew I was serious, he got really excited, and his new energy was palpable. Little did I know he would ask me to be a part of his show. I gladly accepted and acted as his sidekick Gracie. His wife brought in some clothes and props for us, and we did a skit, performing in front of some staff and residents. It was a gift for me to be able to support this client in renewing his love of theatrics, a meaningful and purposeful activity that was so personal to him. Experiences like these allow people to feel whole again.

The Power of Activity

The founders of my profession believed that the use of activities to occupy the time of patients had the potential to improve the healing process. As an OT, I had always connected to the power of therapeutic activity. It's one of the foundations of occupational therapy. *Art is healing. Doing is healing.* It's in getting messy that we get out of our head. This is what helps transform our state of being.

We are all creative beings, and sometimes we forget that. It's not 'those' people who just have it. Creativity is in all of us. It's in our nature. It's our birthright to be creative beings. We were born from creation in one form or another, and creative energy is available to us whenever we feel called to tap into it.

As we go through times of uncertainty, we must remember what brings us pleasure. What brings you joy? You'll experience release and healing when you seek out joy and engage in pleasurable, creative activities. As a newbie to painting, I feel it helped me be more courageous in working through my fears of uncertainty and long periods of waiting.

Getting in that Place of *Flow*

Mihaly Csikszentmihalyi, considered one of the cofounders of Positive Psychology, was the first to identify and research flow. Through research, Csikszentmihalyi began to understand that people are at their most creative, productive, and happy when they are in a state of flow.

When you are fully engaged in a task, especially one that you love, you will find contentment and inner peace. Your creativity is sparked, and you feel a sense of overwhelming joy. Flow is an experience in which we lose track of time and are fully immersed in the present—no distractions, just the creative task before us. While writing my book, for example, I was in a heightened state of flow. In this space, the ideas would flow through me and out of me. I felt divinely guided and tried tapping into this state as much as possible.

Through art, I began to uncover limiting beliefs related to the idea of starting my own business. I learned of the rules I had been playing by and what rules I wanted for my new bold, expressive leadership. I started giving myself permission to express more openly, to step out and live life on my terms. Things were really shifting at this time, and I believe the culmination of the previous things I was doing—getting clear on my intention, living my life, and allowing things to get messy in the creative space—allowed me to continue moving forward.

As I was nearing the end of my art program, I received some of the best news of my life. We already had our second egg retrieval and knew we had three embryos. *Were they viable?* That was the question. We got the call that we had one embryo that had tested healthy with matching chromosomes. The timing of this news could not have been better, with the first day of spring in the air. New beginnings. I knew this was a sign.

> *"The universe buries strange jewels deep within us all,*
> *and then stands back to see if we can find them."*
>
> —ELIZABETH GILBERT

Journaling Prompts

- Think back to when you were a child. Were there any forms of art you loved creating as a child?

- What would you like to learn how to make or create? Some examples may be jewelry, painting, knitting, and crocheting.

Consider making a vision board. Grab some old magazines and cut out pictures, quotes, and words that inspire you. Paste them onto a big foam board. Enjoy this creative process of putting your dreams out in front of you. Display this in a place that you see daily.

Key Tips

Take a moment to appreciate all forms of creation around you. Notice what a blessing it is to have Assisted Reproductive Technology available today. Find gratitude for all forms of art and creation around you. Remember that everywhere you look and everything you touch was born of some kind of creation. *You* are art. Celebrate the magic and beauty within yourself. Each person you meet is a reflection of you. We all have creative tendencies within us, but it's our choice to activate them. Getting in the creative space offers us opportunities to grow. We can get out of our heads and lean more into our hearts. It's a wonderful place to reside. When you feel you're in the mess of life, it might be just the right time to dive into the mess of creating art. Give yourself the freedom and permission to get a little crafty and bring out your inner child.

Chapter 9

Indulge and Nourish

"Self-care is not selfish. It is your responsibility to your future."

—LISA NICHOLS

OFTEN, WE FEEL DEPLETED ON THIS PATH. THERE ARE countless doctor appointments and blood draws, regular visits with the ultrasound technicians and our friend 'Wanda,' the ultrasound wand. It's normal to be doing shots (again, not the kind of shots you remember from your college days) in the craziest of places, and feeling the effects of all the medications. Not to mention the financial strains and relationship strains. It's hard to feel our best when we're limited by our protocols, with timed medications and invasive procedures.

As hard as it may be to hear, remember that you need to take responsibility for nourishing yourself. *No one is going to do it for you.*

If you've ever flown on an airplane, you've heard the phrase, "Place the oxygen mask over your own face before helping someone else." Often as women, we tend to care for everyone around us while putting ourselves last. When you're going through infertility and IVF, caring for yourself is essential, and it should be a priority. If you think it's too indulgent or that you're undeserving of treating yourself, I challenge you to think twice. Self-care is self-love. When you give yourself the love you need, you are already stepping into the space of mothering. Be a mother to yourself before becoming a mother to a new little one.

Since becoming a mom, I've come to recognize that I'm a much happier, better rested, and well-adjusted mom when I take time to give my body what it needs. It's important to tune into your body. Listen. Is it calling you to take a nap? Or to exercise? Indulge in quiet time alone or seek the company of good friends? The sooner you begin to understand the value of this life skill, the easier it will be to handle the challenges that come your way. Learning ways to provide self-nourishment at this stage will inevitably help you cope in the early days, weeks, and months of motherhood.

As you are in the prepare stage of motherhood, I can't stress enough the importance of getting yourself in the most optimal state to receive a baby. By this I mean doing what you need mentally, physically, and emotionally to help calm your nervous system. Let's take a collective deep breath, shall we?

Before we dive into talking more about our nervous system, I want to focus on the importance of breath. This is one of the best tools you have to help support you while in the throes of IVF.

Breathwork is powerful because is it completely free, and we literally have it available to us any time we are in need of some support. It immediately provides calming input to the nervous system and helps us get into our natural state of rhythm and balance.

There are a ton of different exercises on breathwork, and I'd like to introduce two of them to you.

Belly Breathing: Relax your shoulders and place both hands under your rib cage. Feel your rib cage expand out as you breathe in. This type of breathing uses our diaphragm and is a much more efficient way of breathing than breathing from our chest. Many people are 'chest breathers,' but I hope you can avoid this type of breathing. Take 10 slow inhales and 10 slow exhales, with your hands pointing to your belly button as a reminder.

Box Breathing: This was an exercise we used during some guided meditations, when I participated in my first book club. I loved it. Close your eyes and picture a box. Starting at the top left corner, you're going to breathe in for a count of four, blow out for a count of four while you move down the box, breathe in for four, and then breathe out for four as you return back where you started. As you practice this technique, you may desire to increase the length of your breaths to six or eight.

Understanding Your Nervous System

In our bodies, we have a complex nervous system that regulates our ability to manage stress. For our purposes here, I'll simplify. Under the umbrella of the autonomic nervous system, we have both the sympathetic and parasympathetic nervous systems. The sympathetic nervous system is activated more in times of stress or in times of emergency, and the parasympathetic is activated when our body is in a more relaxed state. We are familiar with the term "fight or flight," which refers to the sympathetic nervous system. Our para-sympathetic nervous system is often referred to as "rest and digest." It helps us bring our body into homeostasis, or a state of balance.

Most of us enduring IVF are operating with an overactive sympathetic nervous system. We are often stressed out and in a heightened state of alertness. Just reading this, your heart may begin to beat a bit faster or your breathing may quicken. We know all too well how challenging it can be to bring ourselves into a calmer, more peaceful state of being, especially with all the to-dos we have on our plates. Take the right dose of medications at the right time, attend to regular blood work and monitoring appointments, handle responsibilities at work, while also dealing with the side effects of the hormones. It's my goal to help you increase your self-awareness as you go through your fertility journey and to help you tune in to what your body, mind, and heart are telling you.

Sensory Input and Self-Regulation

In my professional years as an OT, I have had a lot of experience helping children and adults understand the concepts of sensory input and self-regulation. These terms really go hand in hand. We take in sensory stimuli (or sensory input). Then we process it in our body, and we have a response to these stimuli. In short, self-regulation refers to our ability to have an adaptive response to the world around us based on the stimuli we are taking in. For instance, there are times where you have to change yourself or your environment to meet your own needs. Some sensory input can be used to wake up our bodies, and other sensory input may be used to help calm our bodies. The key is to tune in and identify what you specifically need at any particular time to function well and live at your best.

As you examine your own fertility journey, I invite you to get your journal and begin to note your thoughts and observations as we dive into the five basic senses. You can enhance your self-awareness skills by noticing some of your preferences within each of these categories. I'll also introduce some hidden senses you may not be aware of.

You may journal with these phrases:

I notice I ...
I enjoy ...
I feel this when ...

Take an Active Role and Listen to Your Body

There is a lot we can do to impact our own health and well-being. By tuning in and listening to our bodies, we can enhance our ability to get into a balanced state to help us weather the storm. Once you understand the importance of our sensory systems and the roles they play, you will begin to more easily make adjustments to support you on this path. You will find yourself empowered with the knowledge and tools to move from a heightened state to a calmer state with greater ease. Let's explore the five basic senses.

Our Five Basic Senses

Taste

Let's start with our gustatory system. I'll give you a *taste*. Yes, pun intended. Wink, wink. As you know, taste is one of our basic senses for eating. Consider some of your favorite foods. Think about their temperature, texture, and mouth feel. There are times you may prefer cold foods over warmer foods. Foods with crunch or others that are soft. You may like spicy dishes, while someone else prefers mild ones. In addition to food, look at your drink choices. You might enjoy drinking cold coffee, while others prefer a hot cup of joe. There are times you just know you prefer one over the other. I encourage you to tune in to your body and begin to identify what your preferences are. While going through IVF, it is incredibly important to do all you can to function in your highest state. You can do this by knowing what you want and what you need to best support you and help you get into a state of alignment.

On the topic of food, I learned some important advice from my acupuncturist, who educated me on the benefits of eating warmer foods while going through our fertility journey. He suggested eating warm foods such as soups and cooked vegetables over colder foods such as salads and raw vegetables. I learned that eating warming foods may also help provide added internal warmth to my uterus. Drinking water without ice was another switch I chose to make to my diet. Since I love water and carry it with me wherever I go, this was an easy thing to do. I made some conscious decisions about what I was eating and drinking but did not do anything drastic. Overall, I chose to eat healthier, with more organic foods, but I didn't follow this 100 percent of the time. Look up "the dirty dozen," and you'll find the top 12 veggies and fruits that are best to buy organic due to the reported high amounts of pesticide residue. One of my mottos was 'everything in moderation.' I wouldn't deprive myself if I was really craving something. I suggest that you consult your doctor or the other medical specialists on your team to determine the best plan for you. It can only help to become informed on ways to enhance your fertility with the foods you eat. Research has also shown the benefits of reducing your exposure to plastics because they contain hormone disruptors, so I would encourage you to switch out your plastic water bottles to ones that are labeled "BPA free" or, better yet, use glass.

Touch

There are some of us who love to be touched and others who tend to avoid it. Being a touchy person, I love to hug and will gladly take a massage any day. In my occupational therapy training I learned firmer pressure is more calming to the nervous system, while light touch is more alerting. One idea is to try a weighted blanket. Some find the additional pressure of the weight calming and it helps them to sleep. Being swaddled in compression is another way people often feel increased relaxation. Think of being at a spa getting wrapped in towels, or better yet, a body wrap skin treatment. Think of a newborn baby and the calming benefits of being swaddled. There were times in my fertility journey when I did treat myself to a massage, but I was careful to follow my doctor's recommendations on when it was safe and if there were any body parts to avoid (such as feet). I highly recommend getting guidance from your medical providers on what is safe for you.

This goes for soaks in the tub as well. There were times during my protocol when hot soaks in the tub were not advised, but a lukewarm bath was okay. It's important to consult your doctor on these matters. One of the best home treatments I did for myself was tend to my feet. From my acupuncturist, I learned the benefits of keeping my feet warm. I'm usually on the cold side, so I didn't mind wearing warm, fuzzy socks. I began a nightly practice of hot foot soaks. This was a wonderful evening ritual for me. Most nights, I soaked my feet for about 30 minutes before bedtime. According to Chinese medicine, there is a direct correlation between our feet and our womb. Warm feet=warm uterus.

Hearing

Sounds impact us too. Pay attention to how your feel when you're in a noisy environment or a quiet environment. Music has been a saving grace for me many times when feeling low, and it was especially therapeutic when going through IVF. Tune into what kind of sounds you enjoy. Do you enjoy a certain kind of music? Do you enjoy fast, upbeat music, or do you prefer a more calm, relaxed mix of tunes? For many of us, it depends on our mood. I found myself seeking out both. There were times when I needed a pick-me-up and preferred a fast-beat track, while other times I desperately needed something more calming. Pay attention to what your body calls for. Listening to podcasts or meditations is another way to engage our hearing sense. Think of what you need to help you get into your optimal state each day.

Smell

Our olfactory system may not jump out as being very important, but it does play a key role in enhancing our ability to access a calmer, more balanced state. Our sense of smell can be a powerful tool to enhance our joy throughout our fertility journey. You could cook meals that awaken some good memories because of their smell. Love fresh baked bread? Home baked cookies? A favorite family slow cooker recipe? Use your sense of smell to your advantage and bring more joy to your life with your favorite smells from the kitchen. Personally, lavender essential oil helped calm me on my fertility journey. I smelled it on a regular basis and was able to get in a more relaxed state pretty quickly. I don't advise you use essential oils until you've done your own research and been given guidance from a trusted source. Some essential oils may interfere with your hormone levels, so I suggest talking with your doctor and consulting someone who is knowledgeable about essential oils. There are many oils on the market now, but they're not made with the same levels of purity and quality, so take caution when choosing essential oils to use. Also be aware that certain smells and chemicals in your cleaning products and makeup may be potential hormone disrupters.

Sight

Our visual system is another sense we often take for granted. If you are able to read the words on this page, find gratitude in that! Remember that what we focus on grows, so keep inspiring and uplifting images around you. A vision board can be a wonderful tool to assist you in manifesting your desires. (You can go back to the last chapter in the journaling prompts section to learn how to create one.) There is a lot of power in creating a visual representation of your dreams and desires.

I suggest writing out affirmations that uplift you. It is also helpful to have affirmations posted in places where you will see them regularly and can state them aloud. Reading a good book can help take your mind off the stress of infertility. Let yourself get wrapped up in the pure joy of reading. If books aren't your thing, you may be drawn to your favorite shows. You'll definitely want to have a list of some funny and uplifting movies to enjoy, especially during the 'two-week wait.' Throughout your fertility journey, I suggest having some fun, lighthearted shows nearby to give you a boost.

The visual sensory inputs are endless. Consider video chatting with a friend who makes you laugh. Go out on the town and take in some art, or observe the beauty outside while on a walk. Think of ways to enhance your environment both inside and outside. Remove clutter and create a nurturing living space. Imagine the lighting you prefer.

Maybe adding a candle would enhance your visual and olfactory (smell) senses. There are countless ways you can create visually appealing environments that give you a sense of peace.

The Hidden Senses

There are a few hidden senses that often get overlooked, but they deserve our attention. They are important because they communicate some very helpful information. One of the hidden senses is called interoception. This is the way we perceive signals coming from our body. It's how we identify what our body is trying to tell us. When you feel like something is off, that is your body trying to tell you something. It's important to begin to trust your body and feel a sense of safety within.

Going through infertility can bring on a lot of fears and feelings of not being safe in our own skins. Interoception is a sense that might show up as an internal sensation of our heart racing or shallow breathing. These signs are messages trying to communicate with us. Tap into these internal sensations, as they may be letting you know when you're hungry, thirsty, or fatigued and in need of rest.

Other hidden senses to take into account include the movement-based senses of proprioception and our vestibular sense. Proprioception provides us with an awareness of our body position and helps us know where we are in space. Often, we feel the world spinning around us when we're going through IVF. We just want to feel grounded. Proprioception is the system that is activated through push and pull activities, weight-bearing activities, and firm pressure. It's helpful to know that this type of input is available to us to increase our body's feelings of safety and support. The vestibular system helps us coordinate our eye movements with our head movements, and it receives information from the inner ear. The vestibular sense is helpful for developing and maintaining muscle tone. It affects our balance and helps with coordination of movements.

Take a moment to examine your own life and how these hidden senses may be impacting you. Listen to how you're feeling and strengthen your ability to identify if you need a more stimulating or calming type of input.

Sometimes all I could do were restorative yoga poses, and other times, I needed a stress ball. I recall the grounding walks I took outside and the rush I felt from a good run. All of these activities were done under the guidance of my team during my IVF cycle and in between surgeries. I can't stress enough the importance of consulting your doctor on the types of exercise that are best for you. At times during your cycle, your team may recommend bed rest and avoiding stairs, and other times, high-impact exercise is not advised. Follow the guidelines given to you by your medical providers.

Journaling Prompts

- Did you have an aha moment reading about your various sensory systems and how they impact your nervous system?

- Go back through the various senses listed and record your personal preferences for each one.

- What is one thing you're curious about implementing and seeking approval for from your doctor, acupuncturist, or other medical provider?

Key Tips

Remember that nurturing yourself is your number one priority. Before you can begin to think of nurturing someone else, you must prioritize nurturing yourself. Tap into what your body needs on a daily basis and it will get easier and easier to identify tools at your disposal. You'll be better equipped to transition out of a funk and to ride the ups and downs with more grace and ease. Have fun exploring what tastes, sights, sounds, movements, types of touch, and smells get you in that state of optimal functioning. It's empowering to know there is so much within our reach that can support us.

Chapter 10

Explore Your Spiritual Side

*"I don't believe in coincidence. I know there is a divine
order to the magnificent mystery of our lives."*

—OPRAH WINFREY

I'M IN AWE WHEN I THINK OF THE WAY MY DAUGHTER WAS
brought to me here on earth. I feel the stars were definitely aligned
in welcoming her arrival. There is a divine mystery to it all.

If there's anything I learned through the experience of IVF it's that
life can be magical if we step back and let the Universe take over.
First, we have to surrender control. The higher power is here to help
us out and give us the signs we are meant to see. I think back on
our IVF path and stand in amazement at how the right supports
came at exactly the right time—the person I needed to meet, the
tool I needed to discover, the book I needed to read. My journal
entries are a reminder of the greater forces at work. What starts as a
vibration, becomes an energy frequency, which then manifests into
physical form:

> *When I let go, the right people showed up for me …the
> right programs and supports. Journaling through it all
> helped me. I could express myself, let things out, reflect,
> grow, heal, empower myself and empower our baby-to-be.*

There's magic in the unseen, and I have felt this with the power of numbers. 11:11 or 1:11 are common times I see on the clock. I believe my spirit guides are sending these signs to remind me I'm on track and that I'm in alignment with my soul's calling. Maybe you have a common number pattern or a lucky number?

My lucky number has been nine for the longest time. It was my high school volleyball number, and I've been amazed how many times it's shown its significance in my life. I don't believe it's a coincidence that I lived in San Diego for nine years or that the book writing program I signed up for was a nine-week process, helping me birth my first manuscript. I never imagined my daughter would be born in the ninth month and on the nineteenth day. My obstetrician advised me early on that I would need to have a C-section at 37 weeks, after all the trauma my uterus had been through with multiple surgeries. So lucky me, I got to deliver on the nineteenth! If you have a lucky number, I encourage you to pay attention to the ways it shows up for you. These numbers can be powerful signs. We are reminded of synchronicity and the wonderment of life. Look to your guides to lend a helping hand, but know you too hold a key to help unlock your destiny, and that begins with your thoughts.

Mindset Matters

As you ride the ups and downs, I want you to realize the power of your mindset. No one else is in charge of the way you think—*you* are. I believe if you get this concept you will feel more empowered and less likely to lose yourself through it all.

> *Be the warrior in your IVF journey. Be empowered to take control of what you can; you can control your mindset.*

I wrote these words in my journal, and they truly encompass what I believed while on the road to motherhood. I feel so strongly that *you* have it in you too. You are a warrior. There's no need to show anyone other than yourself that you *are* one. Embody this word. Have the mindset of a warrior—strength, confidence, and an inner knowing. Your mindset is one of your biggest assets on this ride.

Take some of the pressure off yourself by letting go of how it will work out. By letting go of how I would become a mother, I was exposed to a wave of little miracles that kept showing up again and again. I believe the Law of Attraction played a huge role in our journey. The Law of Attraction teaches us to respect Divine Timing. Thank goodness I recorded my personal reflections through it all, because it gave me a roadmap to look back on and see how everything unfolded exactly as it was meant to, in Divine Timing. When you're in a state of alignment, the Universe extends support. This was true for me. The holistic supports arrived right on time. One of these healing supports was Reiki.

Reiki

I had always been curious about the energy work known as Reiki, but I became a real believer after my first session. I could sense in my body where I was feeling blocked, and I could sense when energy was released, leading me to feel more peaceful. Receiving this healing involves an element of trust. I was prepared to surrender, while lying on the table, and allow whatever needed to come up to surface. It is a gentle, yet powerful energetic healing art, kind of like getting a massage, yet without the physical touch.

Reiki comes from two words: 'Rei,' meaning life force, and 'Ki,' meaning energy. These sessions often left me feeling deeply relaxed, clearer, more balanced, and more connected to myself. I absolutely loved the days that I had a Reiki session. A good Reiki practitioner will be able to pick up on things and help provide some intuitive guidance. I definitely encourage you to explore this as a tool to support you.

Meditation and Affirmations

You might already have a meditation practice, but if not, don't be worried. It doesn't have to be some super formal practice. In fact, I've grown to believe meditation can be as simple as taking a few deep breaths. It can be sitting in silence for one minute. It can be walking outside. It's a personal practice where you get to look inward, in whatever way suits you best. It doesn't have to cost any money, and you can do it wherever you want. The best things in life are truly free!

You may find that you feel connected to your spiritual side when in a traditional setting, such as a church. Having a personal faith practice can be extremely supportive while going through IVF. If a religious practice isn't for you, you might feel most connected to your spiritual self when outside in nature, sitting by water or looking up at the trees.

Affirmations are wonderful, and I encourage you to find some that resonate with you. Some I used were, *"I manifest great things coming my way. The right people will show up in my life to help me in accomplishing my dreams."* Another one was, *"I have faith that all things will unfold in the right way they're meant to be."* You can get really creative in how you want to display affirmations that resonate with you. I wrote my affirmations on cards that I had painted from my art sessions. These affirmations were a visual reminder I was being supported during my journey. I became a magnet for the right supports to come to me. When you write them out and state them aloud, they can become a powerful tool for you.

Sacred Healing Plants

Incorporating the use of sacred healing plants is another supportive tool that may assist you in getting into a deeper state of relaxation. Two of my favorites are sage and palo santo. I learned of the power of burning these plants after going through IVF and only wish I had known of them sooner. When you burn these plants, it creates a smoke or smudge that acts as a powerful form of healing when used consciously. The smudge from the sage clears heavy, negative, stagnant, or stuck energy to help you create a cleaner and clearer environment where new energy can be brought in. Palo santo is beneficial to use as you set an intention. The smoke from this wood can help infuse a space with positivity so you feel more grounded. You can enhance a space, an object, or yourself with new energy. If you're open to using these healing plants, I encourage you to incorporate them in your fertility journey. You may discover a greater sense of peace and clarity, a new energy, and an openness to receive. With this openness there is more space for serendipitous moments to manifest in your reality.

Serendipitous Moments

Embrace the magic of serendipity. This is one of my favorite words. What is serendipity? It's the manifestation of those miraculous moments and signs that appear when you're not looking, yet were placed in your path for a reason that enhances your life. It's those meant-to-be or accidental moments when something wonderful happens.

I'll never forget the day I showed up for my first acupuncture appointment. I was about to enter the elevator when I noticed a woman who looked very familiar. I said, *"Didn't we go to high school together?"* (Our high school was large, with over 500 students in our graduating class.) She smiled, and I noticed her glowing, pregnant belly. She said, *"Yes! I think we did!"* You guessed it. She and I were both headed to the same office. I knew it was no coincidence that we happened to bump into one another. I received a note from her after my appointment, offering to be someone I could talk to as a source of support. I did reach out, and she was an invaluable support to me along our IVF journey. I can't imagine if that scenario had never happened. She helped me more than she knows. Those chance meetings with the right people reaffirm that we're on the right path.

Bring on the High Vibes

When you start listening to the nudges and following them, you'll be led to some pretty magical people. Think of the friends in your life. Do you have friends who radiate positive energy or a 'high vibe' feel when you're in their presence? Do you feel more alive, more energetic, maybe even more electric? You're going to want to start paying attention to the people you're allowing into your space. Who you surround yourself with while going through fertility challenges can make or break you. Choose those who are positive, supportive, and encouraging, or high vibe, not those who drain your energy or bring you down. The same goes for what you're consuming on social media. Be mindful of what you're feeding your brain and attracting into your space. If you feel drained, discouraged, or more depressed following someone's feed, it's time to take a break or unfollow them.

When you've got a strong sense of self-awareness, you'll learn what you'll tolerate and what you won't. I knew I wasn't going to surround myself with negative people. Those with a low vibe can often be found complaining and may not have a lot of positive things to say about the current state of their lives. It's natural for each of us to experience challenges in life, but if this is a recurrent pattern or theme, then you may want to rethink how much time or energy you're giving to these individuals. I couldn't afford to let myself go to that place. Nobody has time for 'energy vampires.' It takes setting strong boundaries and recognizing that your time and energy are precious.

When you're in a state of alignment, you understand what feels right to you. You know when to say *hell yes* and when to say *hell no*. If everyone listened to their inner wisdom, the world would be transformed. Through the journaling prompts I've included in this book, you will further connect to this inner wisdom to help guide you on this path. As you explore your inner life through the process of journaling, you may begin to see how your thoughts are impacting your reality.

For example, you might repeatedly be telling yourself that your infertility journey is full of struggles or that you have no power in this process. These limiting beliefs do not deserve to be your primary way of thinking.

By addressing these deep beliefs, we see what no longer serves us and can begin to release the old patterns holding us back. Getting clear about what we want to create in our lives reminds us that we can change the narrative and use our power within. Listen to your soul's calling and claim it.

Our Soul Work

The calling of your soul wants to be birthed through you. Set it free. By letting go, we can start to bring in new beliefs to shift us in a hopeful direction on our paths. The more we release, the more our gifts can be revealed to the world. I loved reading Gabby Bernstein's book *The Universe Has Your Back* during my family's fertility journey. In it, she says to surrender and then surrender some more.

As you let go of trying to control things that are out of your control and as you surrender to the process, I encourage you to focus more on experiencing joy, in whatever ways work for you. Our souls are calling us to do this kind of work. With joy, we experience a playfulness that is in our nature. By getting in a fun, playful state, we spark the magic that lies within us and all around us.

The inner work is continual. We are ever evolving and moving into higher states of consciousness. As we learn these key concepts of getting into alignment and shifting our mindset, we begin to be led in a direction of ease and flow.

There are so many benefits to having a spiritual practice of your own. When you think outside of the box, you may discover some new supports that can aid you on your fertility journey. My hope is that you will feel more at peace and more comforted as you continue on your path to motherhood. Don't let your infertility rob you of the magic, awe, and wonder happening right now. It exists. No doubt there will be bumps along your IVF journey, but you'll be better equipped to ride them when you feel more connected to yourself and the miracle of being alive.

Journaling Prompts

- What's something that may seem 'woo woo' that you want to explore? Do you feel any resistance to explore this? If so, why?

- Name some new ways to bring a greater sense of spirituality to your IVF journey.

- Can you envision your future with your baby in your arms?

- What does the nursery look like? Get specific. If a clear image doesn't come to mind, what are the feelings you want to feel when you're standing in this space?

- Make a list of items you might want to buy for your baby. When you're out shopping and see something that truly excites you, I encourage you to get it. Hold onto these meaningful objects that bring you to a deeper connection with your baby-to-be.

- Write about what it feels like to be very pregnant. Perhaps you feel a warmth, a glow, and total gratitude for your little one growing inside you.

Key Tips

Take time to get present in your body. Get quiet and *feel*. Notice if you are reacting to things happening to you. We have infinite possibilities. It takes asking, believing, and receiving. Set your intention, and then let it go. It's mind-blowing when you realize all the power you truly do have. You can create anything in your life. We literally are creating all the time, and it helps to get in a high-vibe state of being. The Universe is there for you, ready, waiting, and willing to help.

Chapter II

Gather Your Support Team

"We are hardwired to connect with others; it's what gives purpose and meaning to our lives, and without it there is suffering."

—BRENÉ BROWN

THE SUPPORT WE GET FROM OUR CONNECTION WITH OTHERS enables us to get through various trials in life. We're not meant to go it all alone. We need one another. I know I wouldn't be who I am today without the strong foundation of support I received from my parents. From my initial entry into life, they were my very first role models.

Not everyone has a close relationship with their parents, but mine were a big basis of support during our IVF journey. My parents were married for 46 years and exemplified what a true partnership looks like. As I was an only child, they were each a solid rock for me during the highs and lows of my journey toward motherhood.

It's wonderful to have loved ones who support your dreams and desire to pursue new things. I bet you can think of people who've been an example of strength, courage, hope, or encouragement in your life. Maybe it's not your parents, but it could be a brother, sister, aunt, grandparent, cousin, godparent, boss, or friend. Look at the quality of these people and what they've brought to your life. Calling upon the people who love and support you makes all the difference during times of struggle.

Infertility can also strain the relationships we have with our loved ones. For example, your parents may be feeling the loss of the possibility of one day becoming grandparents. The strains of infertility can affect multiple family members. Keep a network of loved ones, who feel safe and supportive, close to you. Those who truly care about you will stand by your side without creating any added pressure.

Sisterhood Tribe and Intention Circles

Being with women who uplift you and raise your vibe is essential when going through infertility challenges and for going through life in general. A strong support system is essential. It's time to lean on some strong warrior women.

One of the incredible opportunities I had in our fertility journey was to attend two intention circles that were hosted by a friend of mine. Both of them occurred just after the new year in 2016 and 2017.

> *2016 is going to be my year. A year of personal growth like I've never known. I want to actualize my dream of becoming a mother. Just knowing we have four embryos is one of the most exciting things that has ever happened in my life. This year will be a transformative one.*

Indeed, it was. My theme words for 2016 were *change* and *presence*. Boy, did that year bring a whole lot of both, in a profound and unexpected way. You know our story of disappointment when we discovered none of our embryos were healthy, and we had to begin again. Little did I know how much I would truly embrace the themes I had written—*change* and *presence*.

Having a sisterhood enriches our lives by helping us grow and connect more with ourselves and each other. I was excited when I got the invitation to my friend's second sisterhood circle. This one was at the start of 2017, when I had gone through all of the surgeries and knew we had one frozen embryo. We had passed the chromosomal matching test and were so eager for the next step. Our embryo transfer would be happening in just a few weeks.

Her invitation read: *"I want the richness of our circle to set a flame in our hearts, to experience a shared and ignited torch that carries us through the new year with Intention."* These words spoke to me. I was getting closer to the dream of becoming a mama. It was within my reach, and I was holding on with so much hope and so much excitement in anticipation of what was ahead.

Know that your tribe of women is there to lift you up, to be a life support when you feel you can't quite catch your breath. I recall an exercise we did as a group where we were asked to contemplate the following questions:

> *What do you need to release? What do you need to receive?*

> *What intentions do you want to create? What actions would take you there?*

> *What are you most excited about in your life **right now**?*

This time my theme words included *faith, trust, surrender,* and *motherhood.* Take a moment and answer the above questions in your journal. My journal entry read:

> *This new year, 2017, I want to grow deeper into myself. The inner work is what it's all about. This past year has given me an immense gift—of perseverance, of faith, letting go, believing, surrendering. I want to grow and always continue moving forward.*

Surround yourself with a tribe of women who support your personal growth and development. You may find them through Facebook groups, Meetup groups, or by searching various hashtags aligned with your topic of interest. We're here to lift one another up to become the highest version of ourselves. We encourage one another to dream the life we imagine. Below is an exercise I love to use to manifest new things in my life.

Manifesting Exercise

- Take out a notecard. On one side, write the word, or words, that you want to bring forth.

- On the other side, write a brief note to yourself stating where you desire to be in one year. Clearly visualize and describe the dream you will be living in one year. What has happened? How do you feel? What do you see? It helps to write in the affirmative. It may be something like: *I'm holding my hand on my pregnant belly and feeling my baby inside of me. We've made it this far and my baby is healthy. I feel confident and energized, and I am so excited to meet my little one.*

- Put this note in an envelope, seal it, and write an 'open

now date' on it. You may also give this sealed envelope to a loved one who will mail it back to you in one year.

I would love to hear from you when you open your envelope and see what unfolded in the year since writing your manifesting note to yourself.

Finding Your Fertility Community

Online fertility support is booming today. When I was going through IVF, I was not aware of how much support there was in the online space. A lot of my connections were built organically through people I knew who were going through IVF or through friends that connected me to their friends who were dealing with infertility. One of the friends I connected with was a woman named Rebekah from New York. Despite the distance, we immediately connected over our shared infertility experience.

Over the span of a couple years, I was a part of three of Rebekah's groups. The first one was "Warriors." This Facebook community was amazing. All of us were going through fertility treatments and bounced ideas off one another. We shared resources, tips, encouragement, and more. I told Rebekah it was the most incredibly supportive group of women I had 'never' met. I referred many of my friends to this group and only wish I had discovered it sooner!

The bonds you will share with other fertility sisters along this journey are strong. Infertility is something you never want to experience, or plan for, but when you find your people, it encourages you to keep going. Together we share our joys and our heartbreak. Sometimes you might find yourself opening up to complete strangers. It's times like these where you break down walls around shame, guilt, and isolation and build new bridges of connection. We are reminded that we are not alone. We are surrounded by other incredibly strong, courageous women, and we lift one another out of the darkness. Women supporting other women: Experiencing infertility can unite us. I cherished these fertility sisterhoods because no one fully understands what you're going through like another sister trying to conceive and grow her family. As Brené Brown wrote:

> *"Connection: The energy that exists between people when they feel seen, heard, and valued; when they give and receive without judgment; and when they derive sustenance and strength from the relationship."*

Lean on your soul sisters. As lonely and isolated as you might feel, know that others have your back. Those on your team offer empathy and compassion. They know heartache and heartbreak. They've also seen miracles. May you find comfort in your sacred sisterhood circles. Like Oprah Winfrey says, surround yourself with those who are *"rooting for your rise."*

The Unconditional Love of Pets

Our fur babies can also be a source of emotional support (and cuddles). Their unconditional love is unparalleled. During the course of our entire journey through IVF, I had a lovable, loyal companion by my side through it all, our dog Ace. Sadly, while I was writing this book, he had to be put to rest. I cannot tell you the amount of love he gave me, which carried me through some of my hardest days. I imagine you can relate if you've had a pet with you through some of the significant times in your life. Our pets ride with us on the highs, and they also ride with us on the lows. If you have a pet, hold them tight. They will be a saving grace for you when you feel your lowest. You don't have to worry about your pet talking back or giving unsolicited advice. He or she is there to snuggle and just *be* with you. That's often all we really want—just to be.

Journaling Prompts

- Write a list of five things you are grateful for. You may make this a daily habit.

- Where do you currently have support in your life? Who are the go-to people you reach out to in times of struggle?

- Make a list of potential opportunities where you could connect with others, perhaps online or in a local community.

- Write a letter to a friend or family member and consider sharing your fertility journey with them. You'd be amazed at how freeing it is to share vulnerably with those you trust.

Key Tips

Do you know others struggling with fertility? I suggest starting within your own network.

- Reach out to a fellow fertility sister. If you don't know of anyone personally, you may find that the more open you are in sharing your story, the more others will open to you and connect you with others in a similar place.

- Visit the National Infertility Association's website, Resolve. com, for resources and events in your area.

- Ask your fertility clinic if they offer a support group.

- Check out Meetup.com and search for a support group.

- Search for "Infertility" and "IVF" online through Facebook and Instagram. There are so many groups and people to follow. My advice is to be mindful before jumping all in. You may become overwhelmed by all the input people share, which ultimately may bring you more worry than support. I'm glad I didn't search anything on Instagram when I was going through IVF. My Facebook group and other tribes of uplifting women were just what I needed.

- Look into various podcasts on the topic of infertility. There are too many to name, but they can be very helpful in providing a different feeling of community.

Remember that the more you open up to others about your struggles, the more support will flood your way. We are meant for connection, and we do not need to make this journey any harder by thinking we have to do it all alone. Your fertility sisters understand you like no one else can.

Chapter 12

Keep Moving Onward, Warrior

"When we deny the story, it defines us. When we own the story, we can write a brave new ending."

—BRENÉ BROWN

I'M GOING TO LAY SOME TRUTH BOMBS ON YOU.

Your fertility journey may just be one of the biggest gifts you have ever received. This was true for me. Own your journey. You have the ability to transform your experience from fear and pain to one of hope, ease, and joy.

When you go through something as personal as infertility, you are changed forever. You learn more about yourself than you could have imagined.

When you acknowledge your fertility struggles and take ownership of your personal journey, you take the power back. The power of this journey is not outside of you. It belongs to you.

You play an active role in this process. It takes inner work. It takes self-awareness. It takes a commitment to getting yourself into a miracle mindset. It's really a way of life.

Your path to motherhood can be enjoyable and, yes, even magical.

Before you close these pages and continue on your journey to motherhood, let's recap the *IVF Soul Align Method*. This book is your companion. Think of it as your soulful guide to support you on this path.

Getting clear on your *why* for wanting to become a mother, or grow your family, is the first step. Your intention sets your course. The intention you set for your fertility journey matters too.

Keep living your life and doing you. Listen to what sparks you. Fill yourself up, and know a baby won't replace any holes you feel inside. Happy pre-baby mama = happy post-baby mama.

Tap into your innate creative energy, and let your wild side take over a bit. When fertility treatments are creeping into your every day, every moment, every minute, it's especially time to quiet the chatter in your mind and engage your hands in some meaningful, creative activity.

When you're riding the wave of emotions during fertility treatments, you need to feel everything. Release the heavy, and bring in the light. Your heart and your womb can't afford to keep all the pain, hurt, anger, resentment, or a hundred other emotions within you. Make sure to let it out.

Accept the setbacks that may arise, and release your desire to control it all. By letting go, you set yourself free. Allow yourself to be open and ride the wave. When setbacks come your way, you'll be better equipped to handle the challenges with more grace and ease.

Take the time to nourish the most important person in all of this—*you*. One day, your little one will learn how essential self-care is by the way they see their mama nourishing herself. Make yourself a priority. You are deserving. Honor yourself and the journey you have committed to.

Think outside the box, and explore your spiritual side. Tap into energetic healing practices, visioning, gratitude practices, and meditations. Consider writing your baby-to-be a letter and begin to align with your little one's soul. Once you get into a place of alignment, you will begin to manifest at rapid speed.

Surround yourself with the kind of individuals who light you up, who have your back. A community of sisters makes a world of difference while on this ride. Find relief in not having to have it all figured out—less forcing it to be a certain way and more allowing good things to come your way.

If I can leave you with just one final bit of wisdom for this journey, it's simply to surrender. Surrender what you can't control and focus on all that *is* in your control. Set your intention, and then let it go. Engage the tools that get you into a place where you feel *at ease*. You will begin to know when you are in that state of flow. You've got this.

> *"In the end these things matter most: How well did you love? How fully did you live? How deeply did you learn to let go?"*
>
> —JACK KORNFIELD

Onward, Warrior.

About the Author

LISA WHITE, OTR/L, BELIEVES THE PATH SHE HAS TAKEN HAS led her to two of the greatest roles of her life—wife and mother. In her two decade career as an occupational therapist, she has helped enhance the quality of life for countless individuals in pursuit of their personal goals. She is a lifelong practitioner of intentional creative living and manifestation. She became passionate about supporting other women with infertility after undergoing her own journey through IVF. She is committed to spreading the impact of her *IVF Soul Align Method* to bring awareness to the importance of mindset and emotional support on the IVF journey. She holds a Bachelor of Science in Occupational Therapy from Creighton University. She also attended Colorado State University for her pre-occupational therapy coursework, where she played collegiate volleyball. Her one healthy embryo and successful pregnancy is a miracle indeed and the best gift she has ever received. Lisa lives in Colorado, north of Denver, with her husband, Jason, and daughter, Olivia.

Further Reading and Resources

Books

Activate Your Light by Aubry Hoffman
Ask and It Is Given by Esther and Jerry Hicks
Big Magic by Elizabeth Gilbert
Creating a Charmed Life by Victoria Moran
Daring Greatly by Brené Brown
Fertile by Catherine S. Gregory
Girl, Wash Your Face by Rachel Hollis
Inspired and Unstoppable by Tama Kieves
Living Artfully by Sandra Magsamen
Making a Living Without a Job by Barbara Winter
Moonology by Yasmin Boland
Not Broken: An Approachable Guide to Miscarriage and Recurrent Pregnancy Loss by Dr. Lora Shahine
Perfect Hormone Balance for Fertility by Dr. Robert Greene and Laurie Tarkan
Playing Big by Tara Mohr
Rising Strong by Brené Brown
Self-Care 101 by Shelley Hunter Hillesheim
Self-Compassion by Kristin Neff
The Art of the Moment by Veronique Vienne
The Gratitude Connection by Amy Collette
The Power of Intention by Wayne Dyer
The Prophet by Kahlil Gibran
The Secret by Rhonda Byrne
The Universe Has Your Back by Gabrielle Bernstein
This Is IVF & Other Fertility Treatments by Sheila Lamb
Year of Yes by Shonda Rhimes
You Are a Badass by Jen Sincero
You Can Heal Your Life by Louise Hay

Podcasts

As a Woman
Beat Infertility
Big Fat Negative
Detour to Becoming Dad
Fab Fertility
Fertility Friday Radio
Fertile Ground
Fertility Life Raft
Find Your Feminine Fire
Infertile AF
I Want to Put a Baby in You
*Matt + Doree's Eggcellent
  Adventure*
Mastering Your Fertility

Mind Mastery and Manifestation
Practically Fertile
Super Soul Conversations
The Conscious Life
The Egg Whisperer Show
The Fertility Podcast
The Fertility Warriors
The Hormone Heartbeat
The Infertility Mafia
The Life Coach School
The Queen of Intuition
The Wholesome Fertility Podcast
This is Infertility
Unlocking Us

Other Resources

The National Infertility Association (www.resolve.org)
American Society for Reproductive Medicine (www.asrm.org)
YouTube: Lisa White – IVF Manifesting a Miracle
Colorado Fertility Advocates (coloradofertilityadvocates.org)
Baby Quest Foundation (babyquestfoundation.org)

Acknowledgments

I WISH I COULD ACKNOWLEDGE EVERY SINGLE PERSON WHO supported me in my fertility journey. Your prayers, wishes, thoughtful notes, gifts, and phone calls were appreciated more than you know. So many of you were also a huge support during my book writing process. I feel so loved.

First and foremost, I want to thank my husband, Jason. Our little 'Dot' is so lucky to have you as her daddy. You were right by my side through our entire journey, and I cannot imagine how different my life would be if I hadn't met you. Being on this ride with you is the adventure of a lifetime. You and Olivia are the best things that have ever happened to me. I love you.

My mom and dad, Pat and Bob Czarnecki. I feel your support and love with me always. My mom's spirit is ever so present and especially was felt throughout the writing of this book. Thank you, Dad, for being the best dad I could ever wish for.

My book coach, Catherine Gregory, and her team at Modern Wisdom Press. Your guidance and support in helping me throughout the writing process, editing, design, and publishing stages has been amazing. This book would not have been birthed without you! Thank you.

My close friends and family. Especially Kim Costigan, Sue Brett, Elaine Benham, Prissy and Steve Barker, Mary Brown, Christine & Ty, Donna, Carol, Gabe & Lea, and Ollia May. Extended family and friends from coast to coast: Rachel, Siobhan, Traci, Sandra,

Shelly, Susan, Meghan, Yoli, Ali, Branca, Jeff, Britt, Cassy, Jill, Leigh, Tiffany, Elise, Collien, Sheryl, Erin, Amber … (I wish I could list you all!) To my original Colorado fertility sisters, especially Liz, Krista, and Andi. I love you all.

My doctors and medical support team. Dr. Greene, without you and your staff, we would not have Olivia. We are incredibly grateful for your expertise, compassion, and care. It is a true honor to have your contribution writing my foreword. Thank you. Dr. Michael Moore for your care and expertise in handling my fibroids. My incredible OB-GYN, Dr. Jill Serrahn, who delivered our miracle baby and saved my life. We are forever grateful for you.

My "magical guides," Lisseth Wertz and Tiffany Josephs. My Reiki healer, Cynthia Landon. Art healer, Shannon Boyle. Magicfesting, Wishing Cards, nursery blessings, art therapy, and beyond. Each of you was so instrumental in helping me through my IVF journey. Thank you.

My acupuncturist, Jeff Faudem. Your support and guidance on this path were a real gift.

My "Real Life Book Club" sisters, especially Susannah, Shaelyn, Carlyn, Amanda, DesiRae, Shelley, Krystianne, Katie, and Whitney. My "Playing Big" and "Inspired and Unstoppable" sisters—Love you all.

Photographer and friend, Britt Nemeth, for soulfully capturing my journey from the beginning.

Rebekah Rosler, for creating the most supportive group of fertility sisters I had 'never' met. You helped carry me through the warrior stage, the waiting stage, and the fourth trimester.

Ellen Melko Moore for helping give me the push to launch my business. My "Supertight"' soul sisters—Jess, Lisa, Jessica, Mia, and Brit.

OT mentor supports including Linda Crawford and Melissa LaPointe. I'm so grateful for you both, and for all the OTs who have inspired me on this journey.

My grandmother, Gail Brett Cyrus. I feel your spirit and presence and carry your love with me.

In gratitude for the memory of the most loving, loyal dog, Ace. You passed during the editing phase of my book and were right by my side through life's biggest moments: getting engaged, getting married, starting fertility treatments, buying our first home, getting pregnant, and comforting me in the passing of my mom. You will forever rest in my heart.

Last but not least, the most precious gift of all—my dear Olivia. Thank you for holding on for your mama and daddy. We love you so.

Thank you

THANK YOU, DEAR FERTILITY SISTER, for reading this book. While writing this book, I held you close. I am all too familiar with the pain you are feeling. May this book wrap you in the warmest embrace and provide support to you on your mothering journey.

You are strong. You are brave. You are courageous. Remind yourself of your power and light. It's an honor to walk alongside you on your path to motherhood.

Stay connected at ivfmanifestingamiracle.com and on Instagram at ivf.manifesting.a.miracle. I also invite you to visit my YouTube channel: Lisa White - IVF Manifesting a Miracle. I love supporting my clients with customized coaching plans. I meet you wherever you are in your process so we address the challenges you are facing together. If you would like more personalized support on your journey, please reach out to me.

I'd love to hear from you and how you've used the *IVF Soul Align Method* to support you on your path to motherhood. Please send me a message and let me know!

All my love to you and your little one,

Made in the USA
Monee, IL
14 December 2023

49210464R00080